S0-FJR-734

	DATE DUE		
MAR 9 '98	OCT 04 2012		
APR 7 '98			
MAY 19 '98	SEP 27 2013		
MAR 2 9 1999			
MAY 0 8 2000			
APR 2 6 2002			
MAY 1 4 2002			
APR 2 7 2004			
OCT 0 5 2010			
OCT 0 5 2011			

595.7
JAQ   Jaques, H.E.
         How to know the
         insects

Pictured Key Nature Series

How To Know

THE INSECTS

An illustrated key to the more common families of insects, with suggestions for collecting, mounting and studying them.

H. E. JAQUES
Professor of Biology
Iowa Wesleyan College

Second Edition

WM. C. BROWN COMPANY PUBLISHERS
135 SOUTH LOCUST STREET • DUBUQUE, IOWA 52003

THE PICTURED-KEY NATURE SERIES

"How to Know the Insects," Jaques, 1947

"Living Things—How to Know Them," Jaques, 1946

"How to Know the Trees," Jaques, 1946

"Plant Families—How to Know Them," Jaques, 1948

"How to Know the Economic Plants," Jaques, 1948, 1958

"How to Know the Spring Flowers," Cuthbert, 1943, 1949

"How to Know the Mosses and Liverworts," Conard, 1944, 1956

"How to Know the Land Birds," Jaques, 1947

"How to Know the Fall Flowers," Cuthbert, 1948

"How to Know the Immature Insects," Chu, 1949

"How to Know the Protozoa," Jahn, 1949

"How to Know the Mammals," Booth, 1949

"How to Know the Beetles," Jaques, 1951

"How to Know the Spiders," Kaston, 1952

"How to Know the Grasses," Pohl, 1953

"How to Know the Fresh-Water Algae," Prescott, 1954

"How to Know the Western Trees," Baerg, 1955

"How to Know the Seaweeds," Dawson, 1956

"How to Know the Freshwater Fishes," Eddy, 1957

"How to Know the Weeds," Jaques, 1959

"How to Know the Water Birds," Jaques-Ollivier, 1960

"How to Know the Butterflies," Ehrlich, 1961

"How to Know the Eastern Land Snails," Burch, 1962

"How to Know the Grasshoppers," Helfer, 1963

"How to Know the Cacti," Dawson, 1963

Other Subjects in Preparation

Printed in U.S.A.

INTRODUCTION

THE 1936 federal estimate found 128,429,000 people living in the United States. Forty-four million four hundred eighteen thousand hogs, 11,163,000 horses and 387,251,000 chickens lived within our borders. Our country also had a population of multiplied trillions of insects. Some of these interesting creatures are highly beneficial, others greatly hinder our progress. To successfully compete with them we need to know the insects better.

This book is designed to make it easy to acquire a ready knowledge of the insects. It is closely applicable throughout North America and should be helpful wherever insects are studied. Illustrated keys for identifications of the orders and of the principal families are given. One common representative of each included family is pictured and briefly described. In all, 196 species of common insects are thus treated. It should be borne in mind that for each species pictured, there are many others which space does not permit us to show. When a specimen is seen to closely resemble one that is pictured, it will likely e found to belong to the same family. If it differs in some details it probably represents a species not herein described and will need to be referred to more complete literature or to a specialist.

Many small families of less common insects do not appear in the keys. Had these been included the keys would have become too cumbersome and difficult for beginners. As the student advances in his study he will need to turn to special literature for these less frequent families.

Reference has been made to many keys and descriptions by other authors. Many of the illustrations are original, others have been gathered from various sources by permission, recognition for which is indicated. Our students have made a large number of the drawings from specimens in the Iowa Survey Collection, tested the keys and helped in other ways. Valued suggestions by teachers who are using the book in their classes have resulted in minor changes in the second, fourth and fifth printings. Space forbids any attempt to name the many scientists and others who have helped. We wish to thank them all.

REVISED EDITION

During its first ten years "How to Know the Insects" has served many schools, research laboratories, outdoor camps, etc. Numerous copies went over-seas with our men who fought and won the recent war. Now it has been given a thorough-going revision. Increased emphasis has been placed on the descriptions of families and some 5 additional families pictured and keyed. We hope its many users will find the changes to their liking.

Mt. Pleasant, Iowa
August, 1947

CONTENTS

THE PLACE OF INSECTS

NATURAL history deals with all *living* things. These fall into two divisions, the plant kingdom and the animal kingdom. Members of these two kingdoms, while unlike in many ways, have much in common. Green plants, for instance, utilize inorganic substances such as carbon dioxide, water, nitrogen, iron, sulphur, lime, etc., for food and build their living protoplasm wholly from such sources. All the other plants and all animals are, either directly or indirectly, entirely dependent upon green plants as a source of food. The functions of respiration and reproduction while differing in details, follow the same general plans in these two kingdoms. Thus, many points of similarity, and also numerous differences could be cited.

What many folks would call "kinds", the biologist calls "species". All horses are one species, all dogs one species, but there are many species of birds (robins, blue birds, ruby-crowned kinglets, Baltimore orioles, etc.), fish, oak trees (white oak, black oak, shingle oak, bur oak, etc.) and *many, many* species of insects. All the species (you will notice that the word is spelled the same for both singular and plural) of plants and animals that have come to the attention of scientists have been given a *"scientific name"* and a description so that the species may be recognized when found again.

Scientific names are in Latin and are the same the world over. They consist of two words; first a Latin noun known as the *genus* name which always begins with a capital letter and followed by a Latin adjective (or noun in apposition) modifying this generic word and supposedly telling something about the plant or animal to which the name belongs. This second word is the *species* name and begins with a small or lower case letter. These two words are printed in italics. When written, or when italic type is not available, the scientific name is underscored. Species are occasionally divided into varieties in which case a third name is added which is also italicized or underscored. The scientific name is followed by the name or abbreviation of the scientist who proposed the scientific name. This word, which is known as the *author* or *authority* begins with a capital and is not italicized or underscored. If the species name has been referred to a new genus since it was first given, the author's name will appear in parentheses, otherwise the parentheses should not be used.

Anybody may give any plant or animal any common name he wishes but there is only one approved scientific name for each species. These common names (or as Dr. Lutz aptly puts it "nick-names") are not reliable and offer many opportunities for misunderstanding.

HOW TO KNOW THE INSECTS

Let us illustrate all this. The earliest experience in collecting insects for many country children is with the "Colorado Potato Beetle" at so much per hundred, or quart, but they are not always called by that common name. The scientific name is *Leptinotarsa decimlineata* (Say) and would appear in exactly that form in all languages. "Leptinotarsa" is the name of the genus. It means "slender feet". Other beetles, e. g. *Leptinotarsa juncta* (Germ.) and *Leptinotarsa pensularis* Horn belong to this same genus. The "decimlineata" is the species name. It refers to the ten stripes in evidence on the back of the adult beetle. "(Say)" tells us that Thomas Say, a noted American entomologist described this beetle in 1823 before it had become a pest of potatoes. It was first called *Doryphora decimlineata* Say but later referred to its proper genus.

When nature was making insects she was in a most prolific mood. The total of known species is so great that we must have some carefully organized system of "filing" not to become wholly lost in the maze of numbers. We have just seen how very closely related species have a common generic name. In the same way closely related genera (relationship is judged by similarity of important structures) are grouped into families. Families in turn fall into great groups known as orders; orders unite in a class and classes form a phylum.

The whole group of the world's known animals may be divided into sixteen phyla. One of these includes all animals having segmented bodies and jointed appendages. They are known as Arthropods and include such animals as the crawfish, lobsters, crabs, centipedes, millipedes, spiders, ticks, mites and insects. The insects differ from these others in having just six legs.

They constitute the most abundant form of animal life. In fact there are more known species of insects than there are of all other animals and all the plants put together. This class distinguished by six legs is known as the Insecta or Hexapoda.

Such matters as metamorphosis, mouth parts, number and kinds of wings, and types of legs divide the class Insecta into twenty-six orders. The beetles, which belong to the order Coleoptra, are, perhaps, the best known of the insects for they have long been favorites with insect collectors. They are found everywhere;

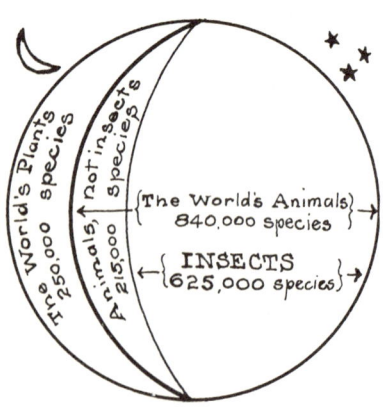

Figure 1. Considerably more than half of all the living things in the world are insects.

many of them are marvelously beautiful in their markings and coloration; they are easily mounted and kept. Over 260,000 species of
beetles have been named and described, making this the largest known
order. In our country more than 26,000 species have been recorded.

Other large orders are the Hymenoptera (bees, wasps, and ants)
and the Diptera (two-winged flies) about which entomologists know
less than they do of beetles. It is thought by some that both of these
orders will prove to be larger than the Coleoptera. The Lepidoptera
(moths and butterflies) have been much collected because of their
beauty and general interest. The Hemiptera (true bugs), another fairly
large order, is perhaps somewhat better known because of the great
economic importance of its members. A few of the orders are small
and only a few species are known but they are so different from the
other groups that they must be considered separately.

The insects seem to be the world's most successful form of life
and many of man's most serious problems relate to his competition
with them. We sometimes complain of a 2% sales tax, but farmers,
gardeners and others are paying at least 10% all the while to the
insects, and getting nothing in return for it. Every species is interesting in its ways and many are so beautiful that their collection and
study cannot be beaten for fascinating, wholesome recreation.

We have attempted to make this book simple enough that the un-
trained nature lover, youth or adult, can handle it, and at the same
time make it sufficiently reliable to be used in serious entomological
work. It is hoped that it will serve to create a more intelligent interest
in insects in general. We recall our attempts at collecting insects
when a child, which were made futile for want of knowing a few
simple things. It is some of these things we needed to know that have
been included here.

SOME SUGGESTIONS FOR TEACHERS

In teaching the use of keys, such plan as this has been found
good. Require each student to collect and identify specimens of as
many different orders and families as possible. Temporary name labels as here shown (Fig. 2) are neatly lettered
with ink and attached to the specimen when
it is named. (See Fig. 31 and page 35).

XI-2	XXIII-39
Carabidae	Syrphidae
det. Berger '37	det. Moore '37

Figure 2. Temporary Name Labels. "XI-2" refers to the order Coleoptera and
family Carabidae. Likewise "XXIII-39" means
order Diptera, family Syrphidae. These numbers may be found in
the list of Orders and Families pp. 117-131. "det. Berger '37" shows
which student made the determination and when it was made. We
prefer to make these temporary labels on colored paper as they may
be later replaced with the scientific name of the specimen if that is
determined. If the family of each specimen, when determined, is
marked in the list of Orders and Families (p. 171) both teacher and
student can note at a glance how the student's work is progressing.

We have found that some contest feature stimulates interest in this work of collecting and determining insects. The building of a reference collection for the school is a worthy project. Needed specimens may be taken from the students' collections and some of the more interested students put in charge as Curators.

A good microscope is very helpful for insect study. The low power binoculars are best. Much can be done however without these aids. Simple tripod magnifiers or hand lenses selling for 75c or less are very useful in the laboratory or field. The ten cent stores frequently have small reading glasses. Students will find them worth-while.

Insect pictures on charts or cut from bulletins, which show good details may be used to excellent advantage to supplement actual specimens and offers a good method for teaching the use of keys.

HOW INSECTS DEVELOP

LMOST all insects start from eggs laid by the female. These eggs vary greatly in shape, size, color, and place of deposit. Many insect eggs are beautifully sculptured. The number laid by one female ranges from three or four for some species to several hundred or even thousands by other species. In most cases it will run into hundreds, which accounts for the sudden prodigious increase of many insect pests. Some lay their eggs one in a place, more or less widely scattered. Others lay their eggs in masses, then the young on hatching live a gregarious life or may scatter out.*

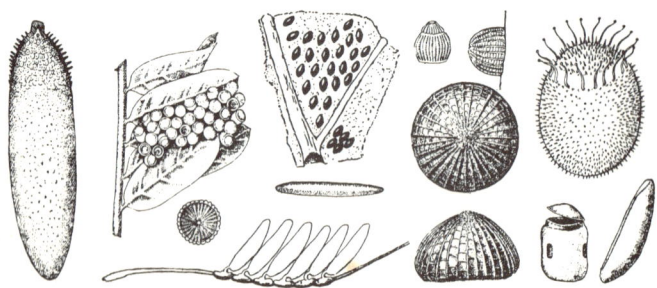

Figure 3. Some Insect Eggs.

---

*For studying the growing stages of insects see H. F. Chu, How to Know the Immature Insects.

HOW TO KNOW THE INSECTS

Some insects such as grasshoppers or chinch bugs when they hatch, look like the adult but are much smaller and do not have wings. The head is usually quite large proportionately, for feeding is a most important function at that age. They often grow with amazing rapidity. Since their skeleton is on the outside and restricts their enlargement, insects *molt* or shed their skeleton from time to time during the growing stage to acquire a more roomy covering which permits further growth. Wing pads appear rather early and after the last molt (often the fifth) the insect has fully developed wings, and is mature sexually. This, of course, is the *adult* stage. Insects which thus resemble the adults as they grow up and change from the growing stage to the adult stage without an intervening resting stage are said to have incomplete metamorphosis. While in the growing stage they are known as nymphs.

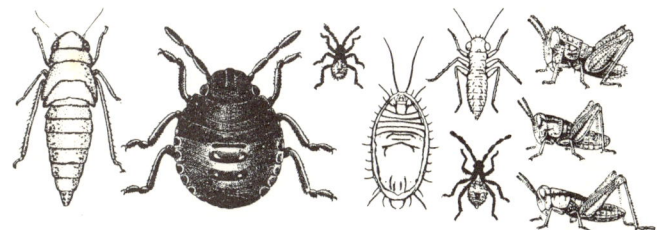

Figure 4. Nymphs are young insects that somewhat resemble their parents.

Butterflies, house flies, bees, beetles, etc., have *complete metamorphosis*. The eggs hatch into creatures but little, if at all, resembling the parents. These are known as *larvae*. All their growth is made in the larval stage. During this growing period the larva repeatedly molts. At its last molt it assumes a resting stage or pupa which may last only a few days or in which months may be spent. While inactive outwardly, some marvelous remodeling goes on inside. Old

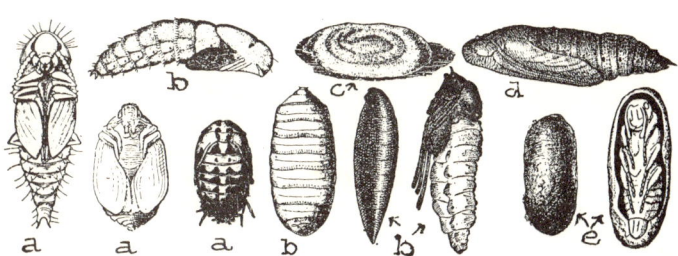

Figure 5. The Pupae of Insects represent their resting stage. (a, Coleoptera; b, Diptera; c, Siphonaptera; d, Lepidoptera; e, Hymenoptera.)

5

structures are torn down and rebuilt into wholly different ones. Thus a slow-moving, velvety green cabbage worm, equipped with heavy jaws for eating tough cabbage leaves, and a digestive system to handle such coarse food, head with practically no eyes, three pairs of very short, jointed legs and five pairs of strong, hook-armoured, paddy legs, finds a secluded spot, hangs itself by one end and changes into an attractive *chrysalis* or *pupa*. From this resting stage some ten days later it emerges an airy creature with four broadly expanded wings, six long slim legs, keen eyes, long antennae, a long coiled sucking tube to gather sweet juices, a digestive system attuned to the new food and reproductive organs to fertilize or produce several hundred eggs.

Or taking the case of a beetle; — the flowers of goldenrod form the favorite food for the locust long-horned wood-borer *(Cyllene robinae)*, and these beautiful yellow and black creatures may often be found in large numbers on these flowers. This goldenrod banquet makes a common gathering place where mates are found. When egg-laying time arrives, the female beetles hunt out the common locust trees and tuck their white eggs in crevices of the bark. These eggs hatch in about two weeks and the tiny grub bores its way through the bark to the outer sap wood before cold weather quiets it for the winter. Temperature has much to do with the activity of these cold-blooded creatures. With the return of warm days the grub again becomes active and bores its way around through both the sap wood and the heart wood. The wood is its food. When growth is complete it pupates in its well-protected wood burrow and later emerges, the gaudily marked yellow and black fellow, in time to attend the fall social function of his species in some goldenrod patch. Twelve months have elapsed, another generation has matured and the life cycle of four stages, egg, larva, pupa, and adult is completed. This change from one stage to another is called *metamorphosis*.

The entomologist should know his plants to find and intelligently study his insects. It is interesting to note how insects also know their plants. The locust wood borer goes to neither the petunias nor the oaks. On the former it would not meet its friends; the young grub would not thrive on oak wood. Insects show extraordinary sense in placing their eggs on the proper food materials for their young.

Protective coloration is illustrated in this insect, too. Its stripes, colors and shape make it look somewhat bee-like. They are frequently mistaken for wasps by man and doubtless also by the birds, very much to the beetles' advantage.

Some simple differences aid in separating the larvae of some orders. The larvae of beetles are known as *grubs* and may usually be distinguished from the larvae of other insect orders by the fact that they have three pairs of jointed legs near the head with none of the

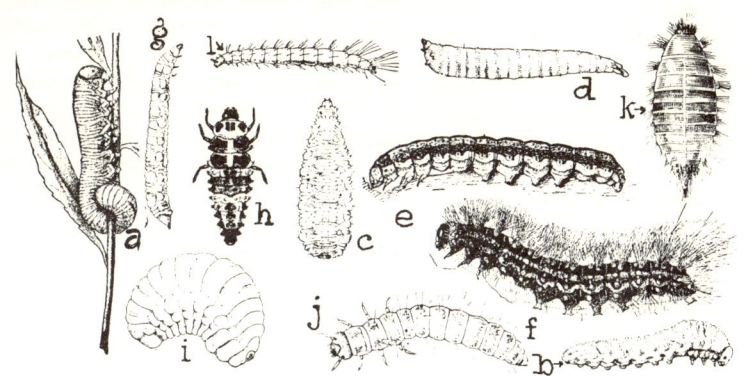

Figure 6. Insect Larvae take many curious forms. (a, b, Hymenoptera; c, d, Diptera; e, f, Lepidoptera; g, h, i, j, and k, Coleoptera; l, Siphonaptera).

large paddy "pro-legs" found on caterpillars. The larvae of butterflies and moths (*caterpillars*) have from two to five pairs of pro-legs in addition to the true jointed legs but always have at least two body segments that bear no legs. Hymenopterous (bee) larvae sometimes are wholly legless, others have both true and pro-legs but in this case every segment bears a leg. Fly larvae (*maggots*) are usually legless.

Adult insects may live for weeks, months, or even years, but frequently lay their eggs and die in a few days. It will be seen then that nymphs and larvae are usually much more destructive than adult insects.

A BUSY DAY AT BUGSCHOOL

REFERENCE BOOKS

THE beginner cannot get very far in his study of insects without access to some good reference books. It is desirable to own at least a few. If that is not possible, they may frequently be found in school or public libraries. Some of the most helpful are listed.

The Field Book of Insects, F. E. Lutz. Excellent for the beginner.

An Introduction to Entomology, J. H. Comstock. Quite complete but more technical than the first.

Destructive and Useful Insects, C. L. Metcalf and W. P. Flint. Particularly emphasizing the economic species.

College Entomology, E. O. Essig.

Principles of Insect Morphology, R. E. Snodgrass.

Insects of Western North America, E. O. Essig.

Butterflies of California, J. A. Comstock.

Coleoptera of Indiana, W. S. Blatchley. Almost indispensible to the student of beetles. Now out of print.

The Butterfly Book, W. J. Holland. Many colored plates.

The Moth Book, W. J. Holland. Many colored plates.

The Insect Book, L. O. Howard. For insects other than beetles, moths, and butterflies.

North American Diptera, C. H. Curran.

Orthoptera of Northeastern America, W. S. Blatchley.

Heteroptera or True Bugs of Eastern North America, W. S. Blatchley.

Handbook of the Odonata of North America, J. G. Needham.

Rhynchophora or Weevils of Northeastern America, W. S. Blatchley and C. W. Leng. Describes the Snout Beetles.

How to Know the Immature Insects, H. F. Chu.

Explanation of Terms Used in Entomology, John B. Smith. A very helpful glossary.

Catalog of the Coleoptera of America North of Mexico, C. W. Leng. Lists and gives catalog numbers for all known beetles of its region.

DIRECTIONS FOR COLLECTING
AND MOUNTING INSECTS

A study of insects may have a very easy and simple start. Keen observing eyes and an inquisitive mind should insure success. Living insects may be observed as they go about their work or may be brought indoors in simple home-made containers. If they are to be kept as a permanent collection, however, they must be killed and mounted. With only a net and killing bottle many specimens may be collected, but a few other items are desirable. A rather complete but simple outfit should include:

1. Several small killing bottles and one or two large ones.

2. A good number of small vials with liquid preservative.

3. Two nets, one light, of thin material for catching butterflies, moths, and swift flyers; the other sturdily built for sweeping vegetation.

4. Small cardboard boxes with a few layers of cellucotton, or glazed cotton wadding in each.

5. Folded papers or small envelopes for butterflies, crane flies, etc.

6. One or two pairs of light forceps.

7. One or more small camel's hair brushes for picking up tiny insects.

8. An aspirator or suction bottle.

9. A note book.

10. Insect pins for mounting.

11. Pinning block.

12. Spreading boards for butterflies, etc.

13. Paper for labels and points.

14. Boxes or cases in which to arrange and keep mounted specimens.

If necessary, most of these items may be made or gathered up around the home. A number of commercial houses sell entomoligical supplies where these and some other useful helps may be bought.*

KILLING BOTTLES

Some compound of cyanide makes the best killing agent. Cyanogas, which is sold as an insecticide at drug stores, may be easily secured and is altogether satisfactory. Slim, heavy glass bottles with wide mouths, such as small olive bottles, are best for general purposes. If a quantity of killing bottles is being made the heavy cream test bottles 1¼ inches in diameter and 5 inches high are ideal. Fill the bottle to a depth of a half inch with cyanide and cover with a thin layer of cotton and a tightly fitting wad of cardboard to hold it securely in place; or the poison may be covered with cellucotton firmly tamped down. Some like large celluloid vials as they do not break if dropped. For insects with large expanded wings, such as butterflies and dragon flies, large bottles with wide mouths or pint or quart fruit jars are desirable. The poison may be put in the bottom or wrapped in a small package and fastened to the side of the bottle with gummed paper. Some use a layer of sawdust on top of the poison and a layer of plaster of Paris covering this to hold all in place. This scheme is good but rather mussy to make and requires some time for the plaster to dry. Cyanide is a deadly poison. All cyanide bottles should be plainly marked POISON and kept out of reach of small children.

Figure 7. Killing Bottles (Reduced size)

Paper wad
Cotton
Plaster
Sawdust
Cyanide

*We are frequently asked where one may buy these supplies. To save reader's time ond ours we are giving a small list of dealers without any recommendations.
Ward's Natural Science Establishment, P. O. Box 24, Beechwood Station, Rochester 9, N. Y.
General Biological Supply House, 8200 South Hoyne Ave., Chicago 20, Ill.
Nushawg Biological Supply, Inc., 110 Ivyhurst Road, Buffalo 26, N. Y.
Troyer Natural Science Service, Oak Ridges, Ontario, Canada.

A comparatively safe and efficient killing bottle may be made with ethyl acetate. Fill the bottom half inch to an inch of the bottle with plaster of Paris. When it has set, dry it thoroughly in an oven. When completely dry saturate the plaster with ethyl acetate, pouring off any excess liquid. Such killing bottle must be kept tightly corked, but will last for months and may be revived by again drying the plaster and recharging as before. Insect specimens do not become brittle so soon in bottles of this type as in cyanide killing bottles.

Other killing agents such as chloroform, ether, gasoline, benzine, and carbon tetrachloride are sometimes used by collectors who fear the deadliness of cyanide.

Many kinds of small insects may be put directly into vials of 80% alcohol for killing and preserving. This plan works well with small beetles, ants, and many true bugs but should not be employed with insects covered with scales or hairs such as bees, flies, moths, etc.

NETS

Nets are of three types: aerial nets for catching insects in flight; sweeping or beating nets for taking insects hidden in vegetation and water nets for securing aquatic insects. All three should be comparatively light but made of strong and durable materials. These may be bought from the supply houses or may readily be made at home.

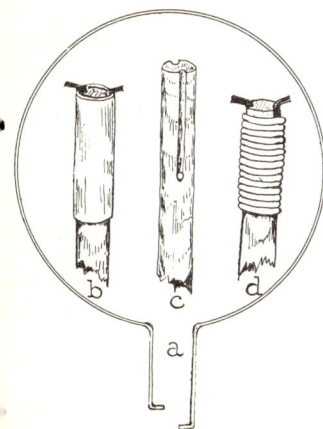

Figure 8. A simple method for making a net handle. (a, ring, 12 to 15 inches in diameter. The straight ends of the wire are inserted in the grooves in stick, c. A metal cylinder b, or wrapping of wire, d, holds the ring rigidly in place.)

A net consists of a cloth bag, a metal ring to hold the mouth of the bag open and a handle to which the ring is attached. The most difficult part seems to be in fastening the net rigidly to the handle.

Figure 8 shows a method frequently employed for a home made job, and makes a serviceable handle. The ring should be made of steel wire which will spring back into shape when used roughly. The metal ferrule is slipped up over the end of the handle to hold the ring in place or may be pushed back to release the ring in changing bags. If one does not have a ferrule of proper size the handle may be wrapped with wire, or tape, or fastened with a hose clamp.

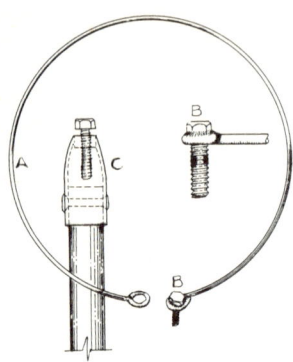

Figure 9. A sturdy net handle.

A still better net handle can be made at small expense by a blacksmith or repair man. (Fig. 9). An open ring twelve to fifteen inches in diameter is made of No. 10 or 12 spring steel wire. On each end of the wire a round loop is formed to fit a ¼"x1½" stove bolt. The bolt is inserted into one of the loops and welded fast. A light wood handle has a closed end metal ferrule which is drilled and threaded to receive the bolt, firmly attached at one end. After the bag is put on the ring the bolt is put through the second loop and tightly twisted into the handle. This makes a net handle that has been found to take severe abuse yet one on which bags may be quickly changed. Either of the handles (ring and stick) just described work well for any form of net. Since some of the other details vary, suggestions are made for each type.

SWEEPING OR BEATING NETS

This net has the most general use and gathers in more insects than either of the others. The method of use is to beat or sweep grass, weeds, shrubs, branches of trees, with a quick vigorous motion, giving the net a half turn on the back stroke so that the vegetation always passes across the face of the open bag. Many insects feeding or hiding on the plants are thus shaken into the bag where they will be found amid broken pieces of the plants. When one stops swinging the net, the end of the bag containing the mass of debris should be swung over the outside of the ring and into its center thus effectively locking the insects in, and preventing their escape. To remove the insects the net may be laid on the ground of in the collector's lap and a little at a time pulled under the ring, thus opening it to view. Many of the insects, anxious to get out of their prison, will fly at the first opportunity and are likely to escape. Others "play possum" or hide among the pieces of plants and may be more readily taken. The careful collector will be attentive not to miss the small specimens. An aspirator (see Fig. 13) is useful in catching the specimens. Chloroform or ether may be poured on the net to quiet the insects. The contents of the net after a period of sweeping may be emptied into a *separator*. (See Fig. 14).

A gas tight box large enough to hold several short handled sweeping nets was carried on the back of the automobile used for the Iowa Insect Survey on several collecting trips. About two spoonfuls of cyanogas was wrapped in a paper sack or envelope and placed in the box. The nets, after being used in sweeping, were put in the box through the door at the end. In a few minutes everything was quiet and the insects could be sorted without danger of any of them escaping. This plan proved very helpful particularly with bees and flies. If one was anxious to economize his time, a second net was used while the insects in the first were being killed or quieted.

In using the sweeping net only a few strokes should be made before emptying it as otherwise many specimens will be damaged. At best the sweeping net offers too vigorous treatment for the more delicate specimens.

Twelve inches in diameter makes a favorable sized ring for a sweeping net. Tastes differ as to the length of handle. While some prefer a long handle (a yard or more) which permits sweeping low vegetation without stooping, most collectors favor handles 18 to 24 inches in length. The young collector can well afford to do some experimenting to find which works best for him. One may readily saw off part of a handle that seems too long. One's efficiency in collecting insects does not increase with the size of his equipment.

The bag is subject to severe wear, particularly around the ring, and needs to be of tough material. Rather heavy unbleached muslin or light weight duck is good. Light colored materials make the insects more easily seen for picking out. The bag when finished should have a depth about twice the diameter of the ring. A quick and altogether satisfactory way to make the bag is to lay out the goods double in length twice the diameter of the ring plus 2 inches for hem; width, when doubled, 1 2/3 the diameter of the ring, as shown (Fig. 10); sew along the dotted line and cut out. An inch and a half or two inch hem at the top readily permits threading the bag on the ring.

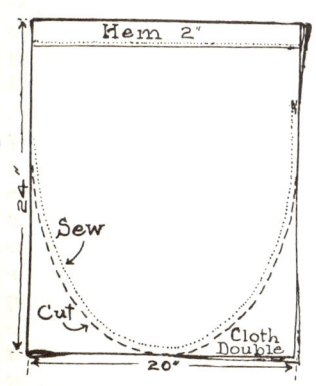

Figure 10. Pattern for making Sweeping net.

Some collectors desire a semi-transparent net which permits passing a killing bottle up into the bag and catching the choice specimens or those that sting, while they are seen through the fabric. It is a rather difficult problem to find such transparent material that is strong enough to stand sweeping and not too expensive. If the cost item does not interfere, a good grade of organdy or, better still, silk bolting cloth gives satisfaction.

AERIAL NET

This net is used for catching such delicate or broad-winged insects as butterflies, moths, dragonflies, bees and flies. Only one or two specimens should be caught at a time and then promptly removed before damage is done to their more fragile parts. The open killing bottle is slipped up into the net and the specimen permitted to fly or drop into it without being touched. The same type of handle and ring is used for the aerial net, but may be made of lighter weight material. Many would prefer a longer handle (say 40 inches) and some would suggest a ring 15 inches or more in diameter. Since speed is often the most important factor in catching a specimen on the wing, a larger size may prove more of a hindrance than help. Mosquito bar may be used for the bag but is not very satisfactory. Bobbinet or Bruxelle is much more permanent and useful. Of course all types of nets must be kept out of heavy thorns and barbed wire fences if they are to last.

The bag may be cut the same way as suggested for the sweeping net but may be somewhat narrower at the bottom. It should not, however, come to a narrow point. A four inch strip of tough muslin or other heavy material should be used at the top to make the hem which surrounds the ring and takes the heavy wear.

WATER NET

Special equipment is just as necessary to get swiftly moving insects out of the water as out of the air. There are many large groups

Figure 11. It requires diversified collection to get the most species.

of aquatic insects and the general collector will want to collect them. The aerial net will catch some water insects but it is very poor economy to use it that way. Its efficiency is not high and using it in the water seriously damages it for other use. The ring in this case is used for scraping the bottom as well as passing through vegetation in the water. Some find a diamond shaped ring most useful. The corners open a way through aquatic plants and the flat sides make good scrapers. The bag may be quite shallow (4 to 8 inches) and be made of sturdy fine mesh netting or of fine mesh wire screen. The screen wire, especially if copper, will last longer, but it is somewhat easier to pick up insects from fabric nets.

TRAPS, ETC.

Man is ever on the lookout to find something to do his work, and even his play, for him. Many types of traps, separators and collectors have been devised. For wholesale results they accomplish much, but often the insects are not left in the condition the careful collector would wish. The appearance of specimens in a collection rates high. If a specimen has lost the characters by which it is identified, of course, it is then worthless.

Many insects are irresistibly attracted to lights; many have an extraordinarily keen sense of smell and locate food or other favorite odor-producing substances from long distances. Light traps work all night, while bait traps offer their appeal throughout the twenty-four hours. Each will catch many species not taken by the other. With either, one may catch species he would not be likely to get by other collecting methods.

LIGHT TRAPS

Insects are being caught by the light trap method for poultry feed and for feeding fish. Some of these traps with slight modification

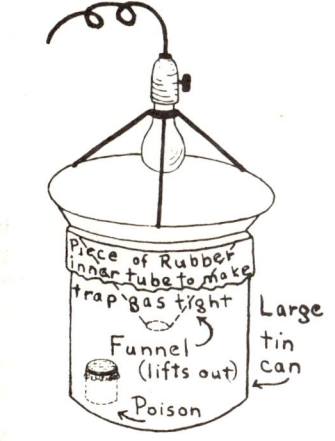

serve the entomologist. Plans for a trap which we have used for years with excellent success is shown. (Fig. 12). We have caught more than 100,000 insects in one night in one trap like this made from a #10 fruit can.

Traps employing a killing jar to kill and hold the catch need less attention but, unfortunately, leave delicate specimens in bad condition. Some large beetles before dying will burrow frantically through the mass tearing delicate wings, and spreading moth scales over the specimens. A trap that attracts, and imprisons but does not kill, requires more constant attention but yields specimens in much better condition and per-

Figure 12. Trap for catching insects at night.

mits the collector the fun of observing and catching them.

An illuminated white sheet or tent with a strong light inside draws many interesting night flying species. One may drive to the woods or other favorite collecting ground, hang up a sheet and train the head lights of the auto on it and reap the harvest, which will shortly begin coming. If the lower edge of the sheet is turned up to form a trough the insects that fall when they strike the sheet or when disturbed will be saved.

BAIT TRAPS

Cans or bottles sunk in the ground to their tops and baited with molasses, fruit or meat attract and hold many species until they are removed. Specimens thus caught usually need washing. Most beetles, roaches, crickets, etc. will not be damaged by washing if it is not too vigorously done. Sweets or decaying meat, covered with boards, make good traps for many beetles. The boards should fit closely enough to make it dark underneath, then the night feeding insects will remain during the day and be there when the collector makes his rounds.

Sugaring for moths (See Fig. 11) may be as exciting as a raccoon hunt. The bait is made of a mixture such as sugar or molasses with spoiled fruit juice to which may be added asafetida or geraniol. An open woods makes an ideal collecting place. Armed with nets, killing bottles and flashlights the collectors lay out their course about dusk by daubing the bait here and there on tree trunks at convenient heights. A paint brush serves well for this. A circular course which can be traversed in twenty minutes or half an hour is good. By the time the last tree is painted with the bait, early arrivals may likely be found at the first trees and the fun begins. Many of the moths will drop into an open killing jar held just below them. Others will fly and may be caught with the net. Sugaring offers the best way to catch the beautiful big underwing moths (*Catacola spp.*). Beetles, ants, and other insects come to the bait. One may go around the course several times in one night to advantage. The same course may be touched up a bit with fresh bait and be even better the second or third night. A sultry evening with a storm threatening, makes an ideal time for sugaring.

SEPARATORS AND COLLECTORS

The Aspirator, a device for more easily picking up small insects (Fig. 13) may be made from a wide mouthed bottle or celluloid vial, some bits of glass, plastic, or metal tubing, and small rubber hose. A piece of fine gauze should be tied or soldered over the tube at (e) to prevent foreign matter entering the tube as the user draws air through the device at "a"

Loose soil, moss, dead leaves, fungi, decaying wood, etc. harbor many species of small insects. Sifting such material through a fine mesh sieve on white paper or cloth will reveal many specimens. A separator may be made which will automatically do the work more completely and much easier (Fig. 14). Take a clean cloth flour sack and open both ends. Put a draw string in each end. Firmly attach the lower end to the neck of a large mouthed bottle. Suspend a sieve receptacle in the center of the sack. Put a small quantity of water in the bottle, fill the sieve container with material containing insects, close the top draw string and hang the collector in a dry place. As the debris dries out the insects will leave it and travel down in search

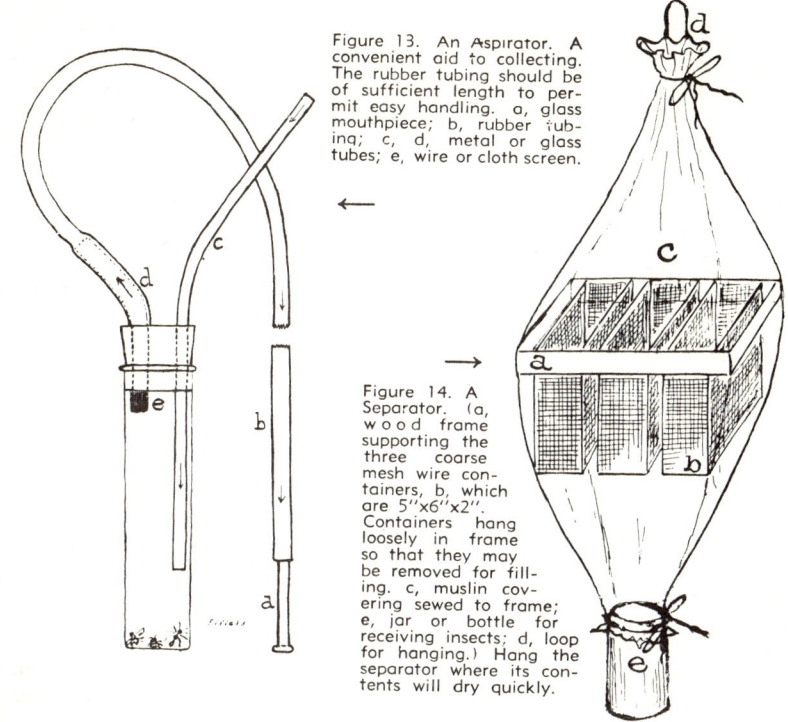

Figure 13. An Aspirator. A convenient aid to collecting. The rubber tubing should be of sufficient length to permit easy handling. a, glass mouthpiece; b, rubber tubing; c, d, metal or glass tubes; e, wire or cloth screen.

←

→

Figure 14. A Separator. (a, w o o d frame supporting the three coarse mesh wire containers, b, which are 5"x6"x2". Containers hang loosely in frame so that they may be removed for filling. c, muslin covering sewed to frame; e, jar or bottle for receiving insects; d, loop for hanging.) Hang the separator where its contents will dry quickly.

of moisture. Many insects prefer a dark place. If the bottle has an opaque covering it will be more efficient for such insects. Others **seek** the light to escape from confinement and a clear bottle will **work** better in that case.

BERLESE SEPARATOR

Several forms of the "Berlese" funnel trap are being used **with** rather remarkable results. A metal tube or can with sieve **covered** funnel in its lower end is arranged for mild but continuous heating by light bulb, tiny steam coils, etc. The tip of the funnel sets in a **bottle** of liquid preservative. The can above the sieve is filled with **moss,** leaf mold or ground debris and covered. The insects fall into **the** liquid. It is all very simple, works 'round the clock and gets **some** species not seen before in the region.

BEATING UMBRELLA

This is a strong umbrella covered with heavy cloth. (White **seems** to be the best color.) The handle is jointed so that it may be bent to stand parallel with the open face of the umbrella. The open umbrella is held under bushes and low limbs of trees while they are beaten vigorously with a club. Many insects feeding or hiding on the plants are shaken into the umbrella, from which they may be readily picked. The beating cloth, made about a yard square, with tie strings at each corner which are tied to sticks run diagonally, with the end of one stick projecting for a handle, serves the same purpose as the umbrella.

SOME HELPFUL SUGGESTIONS

NO matter what means a collector uses to catch insect specimens, every precaution should be taken to keep them in the most perfect and life-like condition. Too much stress cannot be given to neatness and accuracy. A specimen in such condition that it cannot be positively identified is worthless. The beginner would do well to set a high standard for the specimens he admits to his collection and to discard all broken, distorted or discolored ones. If there is uncertainty as to locality or date for a specimen it should likewise be rejected. A neatly arranged collection of insects carefully mounted and in good condition is a beautiful thing, of which the owner may well be proud. Such a collection has good scientific value and the maker learns many valuable things in working at it. Some suggestions that should aid in keeping a collection at a high standard are given.

Killing bottles should be half or more filled with loosely folded bits of soft paper. These keep insects from damaging each other through their movements before they are dead and help keep the bottles dry. A quick way to make these paper bits is to roll a piece of newspaper into a cylinder about an inch in diameter. Then mash the cylinder out flat and crease both edges. With scissors, split a part of it midway between the two edges and beginning at the split end cut off strips about 1/4 to 1/3 inch wide at right angles to the length of the strip. The results will be many little folded bits of paper which when shaken free from each other make an ideal filling for the killing bottles. When the catch is emptied out of the bottles, these folded papers, if damp, should be destroyed and fresh ones substituted. These used papers may contain poison. It is well to be careful what is done with them. (See Fig. 7).

Keep special bottles for moths and butterflies and do not put other insects into them. The scales from the wings of moths and butterflies come off easily and spoil specimens of other orders. Wipe out these bottles occasionally to remove the loose scales.

Have one or more separate bottles for bees and flies, and do not put anything else into them. Remove flies and bees soon after they are dead and pack them lightly in soft paper, in small cardboard boxes. It is better to empty all killing bottles often and to pack the specimens carefully between layers of cellucotton or cotton wadding.

Butterflies and moths should be put in papers (See Fig. 19). A penciled slip of paper showing locality, date, and collector's name should always be included. Insects marked with yellow often turn red or orange if left long in cyanide bottles. Even the most sturdily built specimens should not stay over 24 hours at the most in a killing bottle.

Keep cyanide bottles tightly closed all the time when not putting insects in or out. This is very important. Do not smell killing bottles to test their strength. If a bottle is broken *be sure to put the poison where it can do no harm.*

Figure 15. Outdoor experiences make for happier memories.

Small beetles, leafhoppers, thrips, and many other small insects may be caught and killed in small vials of 75% grain alcohol. *NEVER* put flies or bees in alcohol. Ants should be put in alcohol. Use a separate vial for each colony but try to get all types to be found in the colony in this one vial. Be sure to put the locality, date, and collector's name *in* each bottle of insects caught in alcohol. Write with lead pencil.

EFFECTS OF KILLING

Occasional objections are raised to the moral effects of children killing insects. The body and nervous system of an insect are so different from those of the higher animals that it is highly improbable that they have a sense of pain at all comparable to that felt by man or the other vertebrates. They seem to pay little attention to the loss of parts or to other mutilations that frequently befall them. The unfavorable influence then, if any, is a psychic one, on the part of the collector. Many animals must be killed. It would seem that the best that may be done is to teach that they be killed quickly and as humanely as possible.

Many song and game birds, fish, and wild plants are ever threatened with extermination, if vigorously collected. Insects are so abundant and so well able to take care of themselves that there is no likelihood of endangering the future of any species by collecting. A large percentage of the species collected are directly or indirectly injurious to man but not a moment's worry need be given to depleting the supply of even the beneficial species.

STINGS AND BITES

The uninitiated public has a general fear of insects wholly unwarranted by the facts. Many quite harmless species are purported to be very dangerous or even deadly. Such completely inoffensive and defenseless creatures as dragonflies, walking sticks and tomato worms are said "to kill one" if they should sting them. The story may be akin to the one of a guinea pig's eyes dropping out if it is held up by its tail; but these yarns have given many folks an altogether unhealthy and unnecessary dread of insects. Aside from some bees that sting, a few large beetles and ants that may pinch with their mandibles, and two or three families of true bugs that sometimes pierce the skin with their sucking tubes, there are none to fear or even handle with caution.

These comparatively few troublesome species can be covered with the bottle while inside the net or picked up with forceps which some collectors carry. Most collectors depend almost entirely on the "forceps" nature has provided and pick out their specimens with thumb and finger. A recent twelve weeks spent almost entirely in the field during which time several thousand insects, a large percentage bees, were caught and killed, resulted in the writer being "bitten" once by a back swimmer and stung or otherwise hurt by his captives not at all. The insects that are best prepared to defend themselves seem more anxious to get away when caught than to fight. Even the much maligned spiders (which, by the way, are not insects) that turn up so often in the sweeping net do not attempt to bite. The writer for many years has been putting them out of his net more or less gently and has still to receive his first spider bite.

MORE THAN SIXTY PLACES
TO LOOK FOR INSECTS

Wherever one turns, insect life is abundant. This list of collecting suggestions is not exhaustive. The ingenious student will find still other places and ways to add to his collection. He will get into new regions and try new ways if he wishes to get the largest number of species. Some good detective work will locate many insect culprits.

1. Look *EVERYWHERE*. Trained eyes can find some form of insect life almost anywhere.

2. Look under *STONES AND BOARDS*. (Turn them back to their original position when through, so they will be ready again.) This form of collecting is particularly good in the spring and early summer.

3. Many beetles and other insects may be found under loose *BARK* on logs and stumps. Do not neglect the small insects.

4. Tear up and carefully examine *SHELF FUNGI AND MUSHROOMS* for the insects that feed or hide in them.

5. Tear up *ROTTEN WOOD* and look for the insects living in it.

6. Sift *DRY LEAVES*, decayed wood and other debris through a collecting sieve on a white cloth or paper. Many small insects may be found in this way.

7. Slowly heating *FUNGI* or debris will drive out the insects.

8. On some warm days, particularly in early spring and late fall the *AIR* is fairly filled with flying insects. The wise collector gets his share of them.

9. Have a good insect net, keep it in good condition and use it for butterflies, and other flying forms. It is usually best to wait till they settle. To run them down "tells the world" what you are doing, but *NETS* fewer insects.

10. You will find *SUGARING FOR MOTHS* at night exceedingly interesting as well as very fruitful. (See p. 16)

Figure 16. SNOWMAN? No,—just late with his required insect collection.

11. *PROWL AROUND AT NIGHT* with lantern or flashlight. You will be surprised at the numbers of insects prowling about too.

12. *STREET LIGHTS* attract many insects, particularly on sultry nights. You can often find rare ones there. Some lights are better than others; try a lot of them.

13. *A PORCH LIGHT*, especially on a white house, will attract many species.

14. If your landlady will permit it, open the screen of your window and bottle the insects that come to your *STUDY LIGHT*.

15. At night, suspend a lighted lantern over a *TUB OF WATER* containing a spoonful of kerosene and harvest your crop the next morning.

16. Cut *TWIGS FROM TREES*, tie into bundles and hang on the sides of trees; examine from time to time for wood borers.

17. Visit *WOOD PILES* in timber, wood lots or cellar and look for longhorns, clerids and other insects. This is best in spring and early summer.

18. Use the *BEATING UMBRELLA* or beating cloth vigorously. It often yields big results and many rare ones can be had this way. (See p. 17)

19. Shut up plant *GALLS* and infected pieces of wood in insect tight containers and examine from time to time for the insects that emerge.

20. Collect *PUPAE* from as wide a range as possible. Confine in roomy containers and watch for the adults to emerge. Winter is a particularly good time to collect many pupae.

21. Use the *SWEEPING NET* vigorously on a wide variety of vegetation both day and night. Don't pass up the little insects you catch this way.

22. Examine *FLOWERS* of every species for insects feeding or hiding in them. Be careful not to break the plants, then they may be profitably visited again and again.

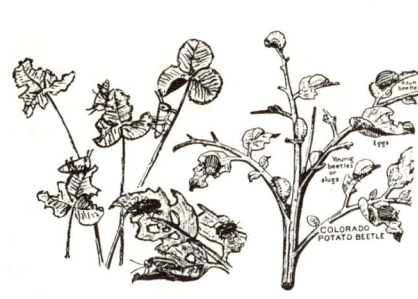

Figure 17   Insects leave traces of their whereabouts in many ways.

23. Wherever you see *LEAVES* of plants with parts eaten away, look for the insect doing it.

24. Look in and under the *EXCREMENT* of domestic animals in pasture fields for dung beetles and other insects.

25. *DIG* still deeper *IN* the *GROUND* for more, and other species.

26. Look under *DEAD CHICKENS* and other animals for carrion beetles and other insects.

27. Make traps by *COVERING DEAD BIRDS*, fish or other animals with boards. The boards serve as a hiding place and when turned back reveal many carrion beetles, etc.

28. Make traps with *MOLASSES* smeared on the under side of boards laid on the ground.

29. *BURY JARS* or tin cans so that the top will be level with the ground and suspend a dead mouse or bird over each receptacle or partly fill with a molasses bait.

30. Look through *DECAYING FRUIT* or other garbage.

31. With a fine *WATER NET* catch the insects you can see swimming in water.

32. With rake or special net draw *DEBRIS* and *ALGAE* from bottom of water courses and catch the insects as they scramble back.

33. Pour water on the *ALONG-SHORE* land. This brings out the shore bugs and beetles.

34. Almost every species of *BIRD AND MAMMAL* has its own species of lice. When such animals are killed wrap the body at once in tough paper. When the lice leave their host they may be easily caught on the paper.

35. Wherever you see *PLANTS* harboring aphids or scale insects, that is a good place to look for lady beetles, syrphid flies, etc.

36. *DOMESTIC ANIMALS* in pastures attract several species of flies.

37. *LARVAE* of many insects, especially moths and butterflies, can be raised until the adults mature from them. This is the best way to get perfect specimens.

23

38. Examine the *WINDOWS* of buildings. Many insects may be found trying to get out, particularly in early spring. Stables and poultry houses are especially good.

39. Look through *FLOUR BINS*, granaries, and wherever cereals or meal is kept, for grain feeding insects.

40. Follow the *PLOW* when plowing is being done and cheat the black-birds out of part of their dinner.

41. *CLOSETS* or boxes where clothing and old papers are stored yield paper and woolen insect pests.

42. *READ SUGGESTIONS* for collecting, in any good book on insects.

43. Lay chips, stones or boards on top of *STUMPS* where trees have been freshly cut. The sap attracts many interesting species and the chips keep them until the entomologist comes.

44. Wherever trees are shedding their *SAP* look for bees, flies, and other insects.

45. When the *WILLOWS* bloom, their catkins are fairly alive with bees and flies.

46. Split the *STEMS* of dry or green weeds and other plants for stem borers, as well as other insects hiding there.

47. Different species of plants are attacked by different insects. Know your plants and visit or sweep as many different species as possible. A record of the plant on which an insect was feeding is valuable.

48. Examine the *DEBRIS* cast up by *RISING STREAMS* during a flood or shortly thereafter. You can't beat it for quantity or number of species if you catch it right.

49. Look for insects floating in along the *WATER LINE* on the windward side of a water course after a warm night.

Figure 18. An occasional picnic and collecting trip can be combined.

50. Many good ones may be found on the outside of brilliantly lighted *SHOW WINDOWS*. Look inside by day.

51. *MOSSES AND LICHENS* harbor many insects. They can be gotten out by the sieve, heat, by tearing up the plants or by using a separator.

52. After a rain look for insects where *LEAVES* unite with the twigs in clusters. They seek shelter in the whorl about the node.

53. To catch small insects in the *WATER* use a test tube or small bottle, hold it as nearly submerged as possible without letting the water enter; on nearing the insect lower the edge next to it and it will be washed into your bottle.

54. A warm and dry sandy *BANK* is an ideal place to find Tiger beetles.

55. When driving in an open *CAR* insects collide with the various parts of the interior and drop in the seats. They are often quiet for a time and may be bottled easily.

56. When dining out of doors leave an open *SANDWICH* on a stump or log and return an hour or two later and harvest your crop.

57. *LUMBER PILES* afford hiding places for many insects.

58. Watch for insects that are visiting mud puddles or the edges of bodies of water to drink.

59. Spread a large cloth under trees or shrubs and beat the trunks with a padded heavy club. Many specimens will drop on the cloth and may be easily taken.

60. Dig under trees or plants for pupae of moths and other insects. Perfect specimens will emerge from these if they are carefully cared for.

61. Separators (See Fig. 11) for extracting small insects from moss, soil debris, etc. get some valuable specimens and save much time.

62. A white sheet suspended in a strong light at night attracts many species. If the bottom of the sheet is turned up it will serve as a trough to catch those that fall.

63. In fast flowing streams hold a water net tightly against the bottom of the stream while stones just up stream are moved or the bed dug up so that hiding insects may swim or be washed into the net.

64. Low sheltered places will often yield some good specimens. in early spring before insects are out elsewhere.

65. An insect net attached to an automobile sometimes gets an amazing number of specimens. 25-30 m.p.h. seems to be right for speed. The net should be emptied every two or three miles.

PAPERING BUTTERFLIES

 OME reference has been made to "papering" moths and butterflies. A well mounted collection of these scaly winged insects makes a most colorful and interesting display. Moths and butterflies are more difficult to handle, however, than most of the other insects and must receive the best of care. Papers are for use in keeping moths, butterflies, and dragonflies in good condition until they can be mounted. They are made by cutting rectangular strips of smooth paper and folding them into triangles as shown. As many of these papers as the collector expects to need may be folded in advance of a trip and be ready for use. Several sizes should be made to accomodate different sized specimens. Since these papers will become moist when the specimens are relaxed later, colored papers and glue or paste should be avoided or the specimens may be ruined. If transparent paper is used time may be saved in sorting the specimens. Some collectors use small transparent envelopes. Each specimen has its own paper triangle and the locality and date of capture should be recorded on the triangle. After the specimens are papered they should be stored loosely in a small, tightly covered box and disturbed as little as possible. For other insects take a stiff-walled small box with tight fitting cover. Cut a sheet of glazed cotton wadding or cellucotton the length of the box and twice its width. Cover the bottom of the box with one thickness of this material. Arrange a

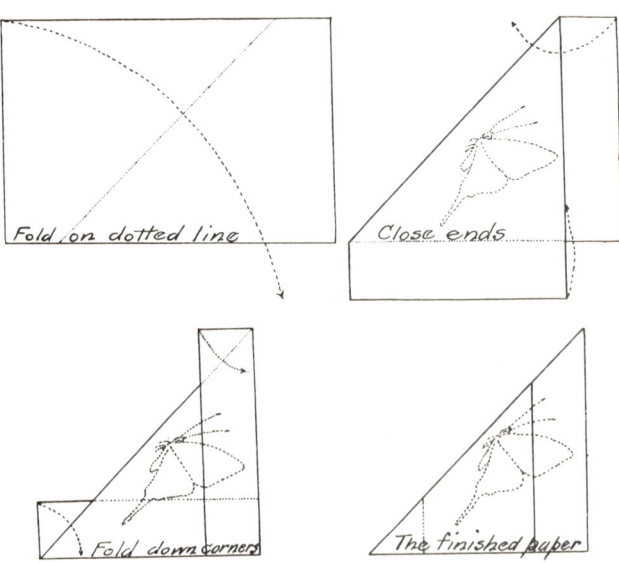

Figure 19. Method of making papers for butterflies, moths and dragonflies.

layer of insects thinly on it. Write the locality, date of collection and collector's name on a small piece of paper and put it among the specimens. Fold the remainder of the cellucotton over the specimens to cover them. Continue with successive layers of insects between folds of the packing material until the box is lightly filled. Do not pack down or use a box more than two inches high. Cover tightly and do not disturb until ready to mount. If the specimens are not to be mounted while still fresh each box should have a liberal sprinkling of paradichlorobenzene or naphthaline to keep out insect pests. The boxes must also be kept away from mice. Boxes so flexible as to bend under outside pressure should not be used. Specimens packed in this way may be safely sent through the mails or kept indefinitely if frequently fumigated to keep out insect pests.

Large insects should be partly dried before being packed and should then have sufficient packing to absorb the remaining moisture or they will decay or mold.

RELAXING

If the insects are not mounted rather promptly after catching they will need to be relaxed when one is ready to mount them. Relaxing makes them pliable again so that legs and other parts may be moved without breaking. For this, one needs a relaxing jar or box, with a cover which is practically air tight. It is filled about an inch deep with sand. Enough water is added from time to time to keep the sand filled with water. A few drops of carbolic acid should be added to prevent molds from growing. The sand is covered with a piece of cardboard or wood. Take one or more of the doubled sheets of cellucotton containing dried insects or a number of the butterfly papers, handling them very carefully, and put in the relaxer and cover tightly. In twelve to twenty-four hours the moist air of the relaxer should have so softened the insects that they may be handled without breaking. The rate at which a relaxer works depends upon the temperature of the room, the size and nature of the specimens and other factors. If it is found that they are still likely to break, return them to the relaxer for another twelve hours. The specimens must be watched closely, however, for it ruins many insects if they get wet or too soft. Do not put more insects into the relaxer than can be mounted at one time.

NOTES

The young collector should get the notebook habit early in his entomological career. He will observe many things, if he uses eyes, which even mature scientists do not know. Writing them down keeps such facts for future use and makes them more reliable. It is well to record weather and temperature at time of trips. A series of carefully kept notebooks becomes increasingly valuable.

MOUNTING

Most adult insects are mounted on pins. Beginners sometimes use common pins. This is not a good practice as the pins are too short and so thick that they needlessly mutilate the specimens. Regular insect pins, which are made of fine stiff steel wire, and which are about one and a half inches long, may be bought from the supply houses and should be used. The sizes are numbered 00 and 0 and from 1 to 8; 00's and 0's are very fine and 8 are the heaviest. Number 2's are recommended for practically all insects. The general collector may get along very nicely even if he has no other size.

Too much emphasis cannot be placed on neatness of mounting. A carelessly mounted collection is an eyesore. In this, as with other things, the last five or ten per cent of knowledge and effort put into it pays big dividends in satisfaction and results. The beginner will do well to set a high standard for himself from the start and throw away all poorly mounted specimens. If characters essential for determining the species of an insect are lost or obscured the specimen is worthless. Through the years some standards of procedure in pinning insects have been established by entomologists. They should be followed closely. General directions are given below. Still other methods for specific orders and families are included in the List on page 171.

BEETLES

Pin through the right wing-cover close to its front end and near the middle line which separates the two wing covers. (Fig. 20).

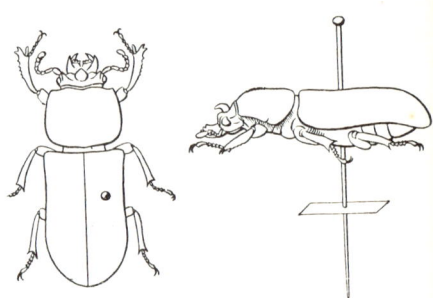

Figure 20. Method of pinning large beetles. (from U. S. D. A.)

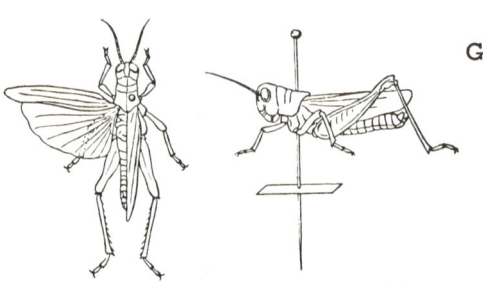

Figure 21. Method of pinning grasshoppers. (from U. S. D. A.)

GRASSHOPPERS, CRICKETS, TREEHOPPERS, LEAFHOPPERS, etc.

Pin through the back part of the prothorax just to the right of the middle line (Fig. 21). It is often desirable to spread the left wings of grasshoppers.

28

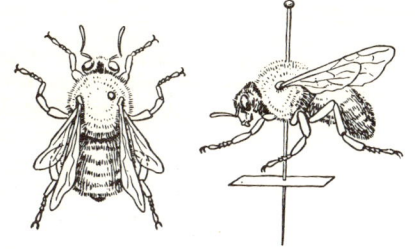

BEES, WASPS, FLIES, etc.

Pin through thorax between base of front wings but slightly to the right of the middle (Fig. 22).

Figure 22. Method of mounting bees and flies. (from U. S. D. A.)

Some slim, long-legged specimens such as the larger Ichneumon wasps may be pinned through their right side. This puts the delicate antennae and wings to the left where the chances for breakage are less (Fig. 23). This plan is sometimes objectionable in destroying side characters.

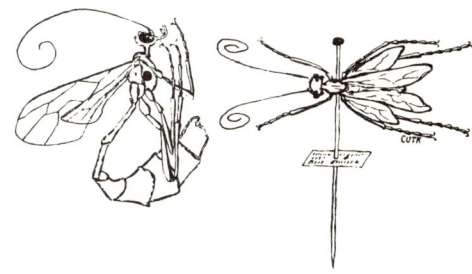

Figure 23. It is often better to pin long-legged bees and flies through the side.

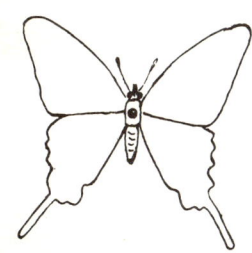

Figure 24. Butterflies, moths, dragonflies, etc., are pinned through the center of the thorax.

BUTTERFLIES, MOTHS, DRAGONFLIES, DAMSELFLIES

Pin through the center of the thorax between the front wings (Fig. 24). All these should have their wings neatly spread (See Fig. 33). Dragonflies and damselflies may be pinned through the right side with their wings folded.

TRUE BUGS

Pin through the scutellum to the right of center. This is the triangle between the base of the wings so much in evidence in the Hemiptera. Before the pin is pushed on through an insect be sure that the specimen stands at right angles to the pin both from side to side and front to back. (Fig. 25).

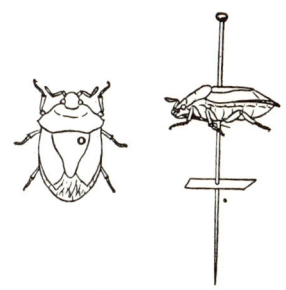

About one fourth the length of the pin should be exposed above the insect for handling. It will greatly improve the appearance of a collection if all insects are mounted at the same height and all labels

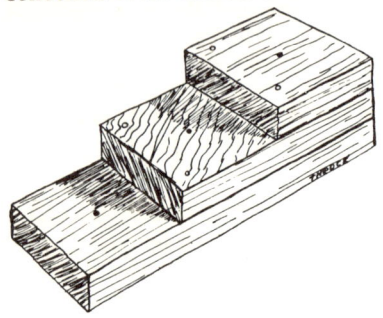

placed at uniform height. This may be easily done if a pinning block is used. A good type pinning block may be made from strips of some fairly soft fine grained wood, 5/16 of an inch thick and an inch or more wide. These pieces are nailed together with brads as shown and a very small vertical hole drilled or made with a fine finishing nail in each step. The holes go entirely through the block. The lower step is used

Figure 26. A pinning block.

for placing name labels. It is also used to get the insects at uniform height on the pins. To do this the specimens are first pushed well up to the head of the pin. The head of the pin is then inserted in the hole of step one and pushed down as far as it will go, thus leaving the top

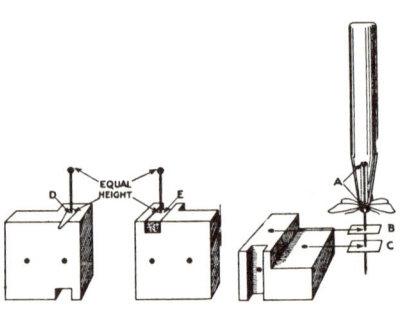

of the specimen at the proper height. The third step is used for rightly spacing points and cards and the second step for locality labels.

A plastic pinning set is sold by the supply companies at a nominal price. (Fig. 27).

Figure 27

When insects are to be pinned they may be spread out on a cloth folded to several thicknesses or on a thin soft pad. They are thus much more easily held in place for accurate pinning than on a smooth table. A pinning stand made of thin balsa wood nailed on strips to give a total height of one inch has

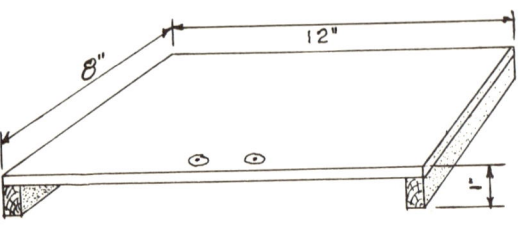

been found very convenient. Two or three holes that will just admit an insect pin are made in the balsa wood at a convenient place near the front and encircled with ink or pencil so as to be easily located.

Figure 28. Pinning stand.

The balsa wood is soft and rough enough to hold the specimens without slipping as they are being pinned. After the pin is started through a specimen and found to be straight (See Figures 29 and 30) the point is inserted in one of the holes just mentioned and the insect pushed well up on the pin.

The beginner should then use the first step on the pinning block to put the specimen back to the proper height on the pin.

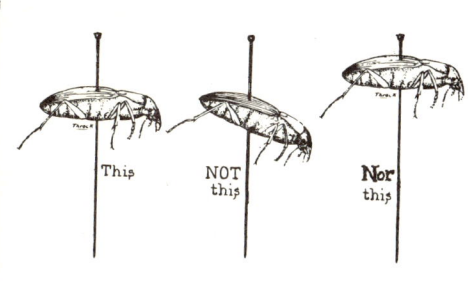

This   NOT this   Nor this

Figure 29. Straight pinning greatly improves the appearance of a collection.

If one is doing much pinning he will soon learn to gauge this distance very accurately with his eye and will need to use the pinning block with only an occasional specimen to hold his standard uniform. The pinned specimens may very conveniently be stuck temporarily at the back of the pinning stand until the locality labels are ready to be put on them.

Butterflies and moths should not be touched with the fingers as that removes many of the scales. Handle them with forceps.

Some longer soft-bodied insects have a tendency to droop when pinned. A small card or folded piece of paper may be run up on the pin to support the specimen in a more natural position until it dries. After the specimen is thoroughly dry the support should be removed. Never use more than one pin in a specimen. Beginners sometimes put two pins in walking sticks or other long bodied insects. They cannot be moved without breaking. Bulky

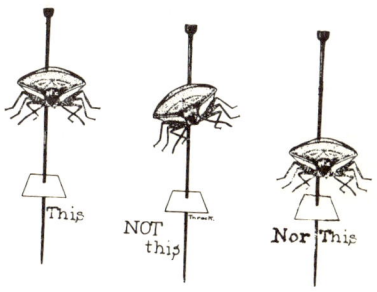

This   NOT this   Nor This

Figure 30. Be sure the pin is started straight; then go ahead.

insects such as large grasshoppers are sometimes slit open on the ventral side of the abdomen with sharp pointed scissors and the contents removed. The cavity is then filled with cotton. This prevents discoloring of specimens.

Cardboard points (See Fig. 31) used for mounting tiny specimens may be spread out on the pinning stand and pinned rapidly. The soft balsa wood permits starting the pin through the wide end of the point without bending it. The pin is then transferred to one of the encircled holes and pushed through the balsa board until the pin point touches the table top. This leaves the paper point at just the right height on the pin. These pinned points may be placed in rows along the back of the pinning stand in readiness for mounting small specimens.

One may somewhat improve the looks of a collection by spreading the legs and antennae of large beetles and other insects before they have become rigid. The experienced collector, however, usually tries to fold legs and antennae close enough to the body of the specimen to diminish the chance of their being broken. To do a really intelligent job of mounting, the collector needs to know the characters used for identification of a specimen and to leave these uncovered if possible.

Insects so small or fragile as likely to be broken or disfigured by pinning should be mounted on cards or points. Points should be cut with a point punch from heavy white paper or they may be cut with scissors. Some collectors like points made of celluloid or heavy cellophane. Insects thus mounted on points are fastened to the extreme tip of the point with glue. An acetate celulose cement or white shellac is better than glue (not so brittle when dry). Lay the insect to be pointed on its back or edge on the pinning stand. Pin the point through its larger end to the proper height. Bend the tip of the point down as illustrated, and touch it to a drop of fresh glue letting only a very little glue remain on the point. Bring the point in gentle contact with the specimen so as to attach the end of the point to the right side of the insect. This leaves the left side, and dorsal and ventral sides wholly exposed for study. Straighten the insect on the point. Points must extend to the left of the pin with the insect heading away from you. Be very neat and do not get unnecessary glue

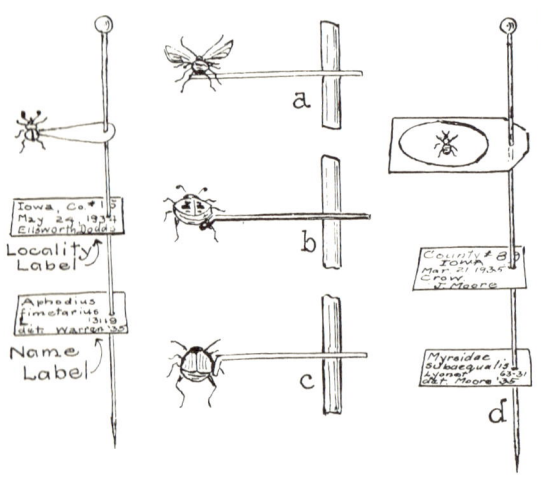

Figure 31. If ventral characters are not used for identification, small insects may be mounted as at a. Usually it is better to bend the tip of the point as in b or c. d, cellulose acetate mount.

on the insect or point. With some practice one can become so skilled that the insect is touched with the glued point at just the right place and it adheres at once and needs little or no straightening.

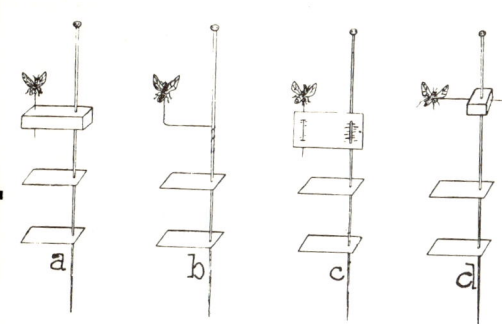

Several o t h e r schemes a r e some-t i m e s employed to mount small insects. "Minuten nadeln" are short and very fine steel pins. This tiny n e e d l e is pushed through the specimen and into a card or small cube of cork which in turn is pinned on a regular insect pin. (See a, c, and d of Fig. 32.). An elbow pin is also shown.

Figure 32. a, c, d, Different ways of using minuten nadeln; b, elbow pin.

Some larger but rather fragile longlegged insects such as crane flies may be put when freshly killed into small envelopes and well dried. A specimen may then be glued on its side on double card points, with less chance of breakage. Turn wings to left.

Two to four specimens of the *same species* of small insects may be mounted on a white card. Make the cards very small and perfect rectangles. Arrange a *small* drop of glue on the card for each insect then carefully place the insects on these drops. Put at least one of the specimens on its back. Head all of them away from you. When finally arranged, pin the card through the middle or right end, using the top step of the pinning block or the pinning stand to get the correct height. Ants are usually mounted on cards.

Butterflies and moths should have the wings spread. Use forceps to handle the specimens. If the wings are folded together over the back they may be opened for pinning by squeezing the sides of the thorax with the forceps just below the wing bases. Pin the specimen through the prothorax to the proper height on the pin. Then with this pin fasten the specimen to the spreading board bringing the "shoulders" of the specimen just even with the top of the board. With a fine pin or needle placed just back of a heavy vein, pull both front wings forward until their back margins make a straight line with each other at right angles to the body. In a similar way pull up and fasten the back wings. Finally pin a strip of paper across the wings to hold them in place. Use common pins or better still, glass headed "mourning pins" for this. Put the pins just outside the wings but *never* through them. If body or antennae are out of natural position they may be braced with pins until dry.

Other insects having large broad wings such as dragonflies, Dobsonflies, stoneflies, cicadas, etc. may be mounted on the spreading board. The long slim bodies of dragonflies and damselflies are so fragile when dry that they are frequently reinforced. With a long slim needle, soft darning cotton may be pulled from the front of the thorax through to the tip of the abdomen. When the thread comes out clean, cut off at both ends, and leave for reinforcement. If colors of darning cotton matching those of the specimen are selected so much the better. Grasshoppers should have only the left wings spread. The locality and date of collection should be carefully kept for each insect, on the spreading board and locality labels put on the pin as soon as the insect is removed.

Spreading boards must be kept where mice and roaches cannot have access to them. This is true of specimens in any form. Mice can completely ruin a fine collection in one night. Insects should stay on the spreading board until thoroughly dry, usually a week or two depending on the weather and size of insect. When dry they should be removed promptly and after receiving the locality labels be put in boxes.

Pinning boards should be solidly made but need not be expensive. A springy, loosely constructed board is almost certain to seriously damage the specimen. Plans for a good board are shown. The top pieces should be of soft wood that takes pins readily. The other parts may be of either soft or hard wood. Corrugated paper of balsa

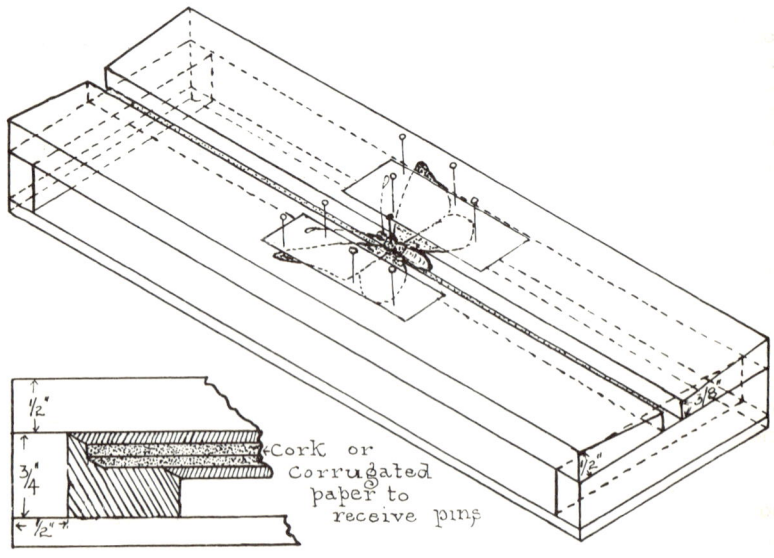

Figure · 33. Plan for spreading board.

wood may be substituted for the cork strips. These strips must be securely tacked or glued into place. The collector should have several boards with different sized openings between the strips to accomodate different sizes of moths and butterflies. A screw eye in one end or other device for hanging the board is desirable.

Every insect specimen should have a locality label showing where and when caught and the collector's name. Labels may be printed with pen and ink but should not be larger than ¼ by ½ inch in size. Printed labels are much neater. They may be bought from supply houses or may be made by planographing a typewritten sheet. (Fig. 34). Collectors worthy of the name are very careful to keep their

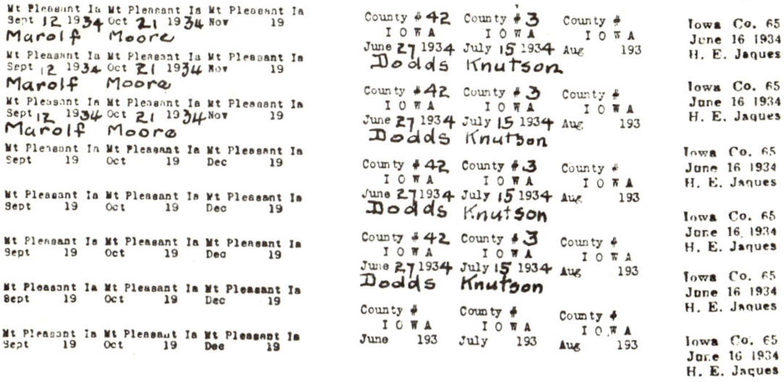

Figure 34. Locality Labels. (A and B, printed from cut made from typewritten copy; c, completely filled in labels, made with label printer.)

locality labels accurate. Labels are pinned through their center and arranged to read from back to front. Where insects are mounted on points or cards the label is pinned through the right end, stands under the point or card and extends parallel with it. *Always* use the pinning block (second step) to get the proper height for the locality label. Locality labels should always be put on specimens promptly before there is a chance for mistakes.

To know the food of a species or its habitat are facts of high scientific value. These may be put in a word or two on the bottom of the locality label or may go on a separate label. Some collectors assign the specimen a number and make a more detailed record of habitat, food, peculiar habits, etc. in a notebook. The collector should not undertake such records in any form unless he plans to be very accurate with them. In fact one should not engage in any kind of scientific work if he cannot be reliable and trustworthy.

At some later time, when the knowledge is available, a label bearing the scientific name of the specimen may be pinned (first step of pinning block) below the locality label and in the same relative position. Name labels often have black border lines. The genus and species names together with the authority should be neatly printed.

With many specimens it is desirable to mark the sex. The label may also contain the catalog number and a name and date showing by whom and when determined. By use of the catalog number, specimens may be easily arranged in their logical order.

Cigar boxes with *tight fitting* bottoms of corrugated paper are useful for housing collections. Arrange insects to face the lid of the box when open. Use a grade of corrugated paper which takes insect pins easily. It is better to make it double. The supply houses make and sell several styles of insect boxes and cases. If one buys insect boxes he should see that they are pest tight. Even then, fumigation about twice a year is necessary to insure against loss from insect pests. Cigar boxes require to be even more closely watched. Paradichlorobenzene makes a good fumigant and is not poisonous to man or particularly objectionable. Put a small spoonful of the white crystals into each box and let them evaporate. Carbon disulphide is sometimes used. It stains, has a bad odor, and is highly explosive when mixed with air.

Duplicates are frequently papered instead of being pinned. They are put between two squares of cotton wadding or cellucotton and folded in a paper. No cotton is used for Lepidoptera, bees, flies, or other insects with large wings. The paper should be plainly labeled on the outside to show the scientific name and catalog number of the species, the number of specimens in the paper, the locality and date of collection, and the collector's name. Such papered specimens must be kept in tightly closed containers with some insecticide to keep out skin beetles and other pests and should not be opened without relaxing.

After insects have been pinned, the specimen itself must never be touched without being previously relaxed. In handling pinned insects be careful not to let the fingers slide down on the pin and touch the insect. Pinning forceps are frequently used for transferring pinned specimens.

The larvae of insects such as caterpillars, grubs, etc., are too soft to be pinned. They may be killed by dropping in water at the boiling point for five to ten minutes, then preserved in alcohol or they may be put at once into the alcohol, which latter method does not leave the specimen in as good condition. A little glycerine, say 5 to 8%, prevents shrinkage and keeps the specimen more lifelike.

Some orders of water living insects such as the Mayflies and stoneflies are so soft that pinning them is not at all satisfactory. They should be put up in vials of 75% grain alcohol. The preservative should be changed after a day or two for best results.

Plant lice, thrips, bird lice, sucking lice, and similar small soft bodied insects are mounted on microscope slides. Balsam or Gum

Dammar may be used. Berlese's Fluid* is also good. The locality data is attached to one end of the slide and the name label to the other. Some prefer to mount such insects on small bits of fairly thick cellulose acetate. (See Fig. 31) A small cover glass and the Berlese Fluid are used the same as for the microscope slides. These mounts are pinned at point height on an insect pin and labeled and otherwise treated like any other insect mount.

Caterpillars and other larvae are frequently inflated. First put them on a piece of blotting paper and press out the body contents by rolling with a lead pencil or other cylindrical object, starting from the thorax just back of the head and continuing to the end of the abdomen, exerting just enough pressure to force out most of the body contents and not enough to rupture the skin or break off the fine spines or hairs. A piece of glass tubing which has been drawn to a rather long point is then inserted in the anal opening of the caterpillar and the caterpillar fastened to it by a hooked wire clip on the tube. Some collectors attach the skin by heating the point of the glass tube before inserting it. The wet skin then adheres by its own juices to the tube. The caterpillar skin is inflated by forcing air by a hand or foot bellows into the tube, care being taken not to use too much force and thus distort the caterpillar. While in this condition it is dried in an oven hot enough to bake thoroughly without scorching the insect. Various types of apparatus for inflating caterpillars are to be had from entomological supply houses. The ingenious collector, can easily make one for himself at little expense. All that is required is a lamp of some kind for heat, a tin can to serve as an oven, a stand to support the can, glass tubing, a bit of spring wire and a hand bulb or bellows and an expansion bulb to give an even flow of air. A rectangular can on an inverted electric iron makes an excellent oven. When the larva is thoroughly dry it is carefully removed from the glass rod and mounted as shown in the illustration. A bit of glue is used to hold the caterpillar in place on the wire. The advantage of this method of preservation is that the larva can be pinned in the collection in association with the specimens of the adult of the same species. When the inflation has been carefully done, the caterpillars present a lifelike appearance, retaining most of their spines, markings, and colors.

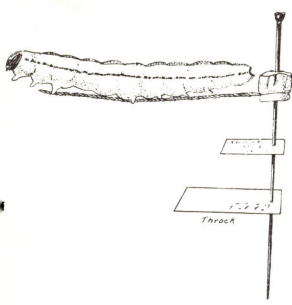

Figure 35. Method of mounting inflated larvae.

*Distilled water ....20 cc
Concentrated Glycerine .... 6 cc
Gum Arabic ....12 gms
Chloral Hydrate ....20 gms
Living insects may be mounted directly in this medium. It is well to put them first in water to prevent air bubbles. Alcohol specimens should be washed thoroughly before mounting.

Larvae too small to be handled in this fashion may sometimes be successfully inflated and dried by burying in dry sand which is then heated. If the right temperature can be maintained the gases generated by drying the inner contents will distend the body wall until it is dried in an expanded condition. Considerable skill and experience is required to do this successfully. Insect galls on leaves or soft fruit can be dried in sand in this same way.

Figure 36. The Elbow Block.

After an insect specimen is pinned it should never be touched with anything unless it has been previously relaxed. Specimens are handled by the top of the pin and great care must be taken not to let the fingers come in contact with any part of the specimen. After the specimen has dried the antennae and legs are especially fragile. The elbow block (Fig. 36) makes an excellent device for holding specimens as they are studied under the microscope. It is made of two pieces of thin wood. A bit of modelling clay receives the pin. The block may be set on any one of its sides or the head of the pin may be stuck into the clay.

The supply companies sell a very convenient holder by which the insect may be turned in any direction and remain approximately within the focus of the microscope (Fig. 37).

Figure 37.

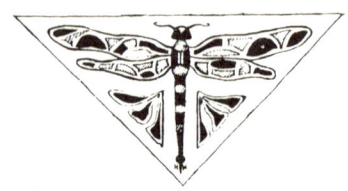

MAKING AND HOUSING A LARGE INSECT COLLECTION

large insect collection must have well planned housing and systematic arrangement if it is to be protected from destructive agencies and be workable.

In many geographic and natural areas, surveys are being made to find just what plants or animals live within these borders. Individual collectors, as well as biology departments of high schools and colleges, find this an excellent means of getting a better knowledge of the insects, and in maintaining interest. A survey collection, whether small or large, on which active work is being done, gives a desirable air of continuity and permanency to a school department. The Iowa Insect Survey, which was designed as an aid in teaching systematic entomology, at Iowa Wesleyan College, is herein briefly described in the hope that the information may prove useful to others. The purpose of the Survey is to determine and record the seasonal and geographic distribution of the adults of all known

16065 XI-102	Phyllotreta sinuata (Steph.)

Figure 38. A Tray Label.

Iowa species of insects. For each species of insect, the attempt is made to keep one specimen from every possible county and to see that each possible month is likewise represented. All the specimens representing the one species are pinned in a cardboard tray. A red margined tray label bearing the catalog, order and family numbers together with the typed name of the species stands at the head of the tray. (Fig. 38) Trays are kept in 14x19 inch glass-topped wood cases (Fig. 40) and are arranged in their logical numerical order which makes it possible to locate any species on a moment's notice. These cases are housed in dust-tight, pest-proof steel cabinets, holding two rows or 48 cases in each cabinet.

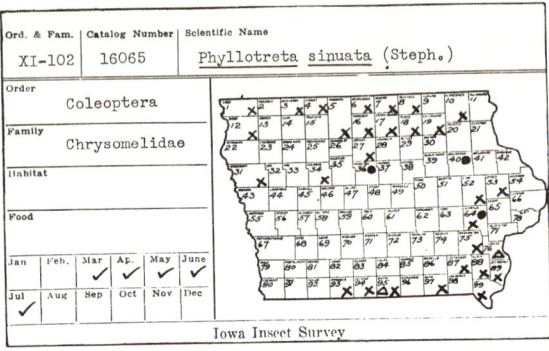

Figure 39. A specimen record card. X Insect specimen in the Iowa Survey Collection; ● ▲ Literature records.

Each species of insect known to occur in the state has a record card (Fig. 39) on which its distribution by counties and months is marked. The records come from the specimens in the Survey collection and from the apparently reliable lists of Iowa insects. Different characters are employed to show the source of the information thus marked on the cards.*

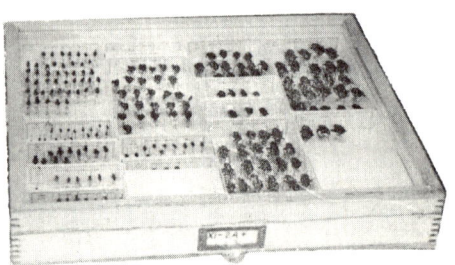

Figure 40. A drawer or case from Iowa Insect Survey collection.

The collection which now numbers some 300,000 specimens and almost 7,000 named species, has been built very largely by student collecting over a period of more than twenty years. It will be noted that localities are designated by county. The counties of the state have each been assigned a number (Iowa has 99 counties) and the locality labels marked with these numbers. Summer trips have been run throughout the state to do collecting, and other Iowa schools Boy Scout camps and others have contributed specimens.

---

* Some Methods of Labelling and Housing Large Insect Collections. H. E. Jaques. Canadian Entomologist, Jan. 1936.

Many specialists have helped with determinations. We are especially indebted in this way to the Division of Insect Identifications of the United States Department of Agriculture.

A very large part of the work of building and keeping the collection and records is done by college students as their instruction in Systematic Entomology. These students, as soon as their knowledge permits, are encouraged to devote part of their time to an intensive study of some particular group of insects and to publish their findings. A good number of such papers have already appeared.

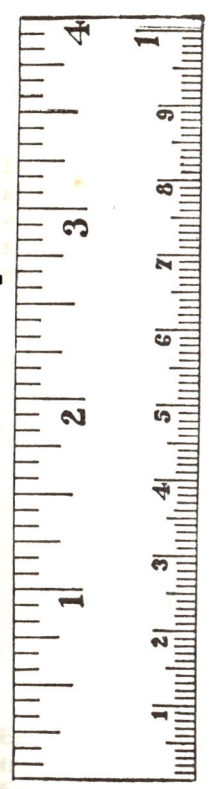

Accurate measurements play an important part in insect identification. A rule is printed here for the help of those who may not have one at hand.

PRONUNCIATION

Entomologists do not all agree in their pronunciation of scientific names. It will be observed that the accented syllable of these terms is marked in the main body of the book, the grave accent (\ ) being used to indicate the long English sound of the vowel and the acute accent (∕) for the vowel taking the short or otherwise modified sound. We have tried to follow good authorities in locating the marks and hope this feature will prove helpful.

HOW TO USE THE KEYS

Keys are used for the ready identification of insects and other living things. They are based on an orderly elimination of the characters that do not fit the case in hand. Most insect keys are dichotomous, i. e., they consider only two possibilities at one time. To use the keys in this book, take the insect to be identified and turn to the "Key to the Orders of Insects" p. 47. Compare the insect with 1a and 1b of the key. Supposing it has "no wings" we then turn to #19 p. 57. and compare 19a with 19b. We note that it has no balancers and are directed to #20. Since it is "narrow waisted" and ant-like we see it must belong to Order XXV HYMENOPTERA and are directed to page 157 where we start with 1a, 1b under "ORDER HYMENOPTERA". Since the abdomen has a slender petiole as in 1b we are referred to 5. But there is no "node or erect scale on the petiole" sending us to 6. Since our specimen is "covered on thorax or abdomen with red hairs, we believe it to be a female Velvet Ant belonging to Family 50, *Mutillidae*. Our specimen closely resembles Fig. 348, so we feel quite sure of our identification.

But since almost every family has numerous species of insects belonging to it, one should not be too hasty in deciding that his specimen is the one described and pictured here to illustrate the family. After all the purpose of the book and keys is to give a reliable means of determining *families*. If the user wished to accurately name the species of a specimen he needs to use a manual of the order or family involved.

It should be borne in mind that keys are neither infallible nor final. The ones given here are designed to aid in determining the family to which an insect belongs. To make these keys more usable many of the less common families have been omitted. If one should attempt to name a specimen belonging to one of these omitted families, he would surely end at the wrong place, if he could get anywhere at all with it.

The beginner needs to know something about the external structure of insects to use the keys intelligently.

HOW TO KNOW THE INSECTS

All of the hundreds of thousands of different kinds of insects are alike in having bodies of three parts; head, thorax, and abdomen, and in having three pairs of legs. The head bears two compound eyes and often two, or more frequently three simple eyes (ocelli). A pair of antennae or feelers are always found on the head of an insect. The feeding apparatus falls into two classes; chewing mouthparts, and sucking mouthparts. Beetles, grasshoppers, crickets, and dragonflies are outstanding examples of insects that tear up their food with chewing mouthparts. In contrast to these, butterflies, moths, flies, true bugs, leafhoppers, etc. have their mouthparts specialized so as to form a hollow tube through which liquid foods may be drawn. Many bees have a combination of chewing and sucking mouthparts.

Chewing mouthparts vary widely in relative size of parts but consist rather uniformly of an upper lip (labrum), covering the other parts; a pair of horny jaws (mandibles) which work from side to side; a pair of maxilla each bearing a galea, lacinia and a jointed palp or sense organ resembling a short antenna. Under all these parts is the lower lip (labium) with its center parts and its pair of labial palps, jointed and resembling the maxillary palps.

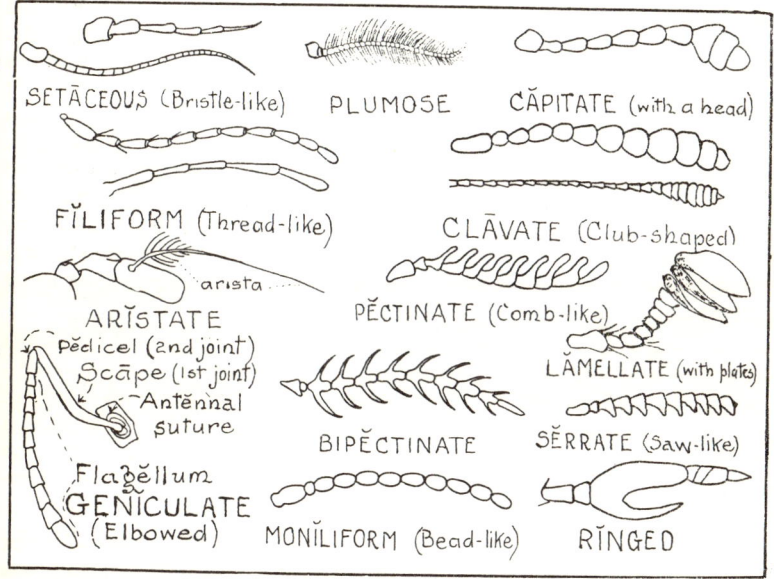

Figure 41. Types of Antennae.

The elongated tube and accessory parts of insects having suctorial mouthparts include some or all of these same structures variously modified. The mouthparts of insects are highly characteristic of their groups and are often used for identification.

The antennae are always jointed and take many different forms, some of which are shown (Fig. 41).

43

The thorax is divided into three segments. The first, or part nearest the head, (prothorax) bears the first pair, or front legs. The second part (mesothorax) bears the second pair, or middle legs and the first pair of wings. The metathorax is the third segment. It bears the third pair, or hind legs and the second pair of wings.

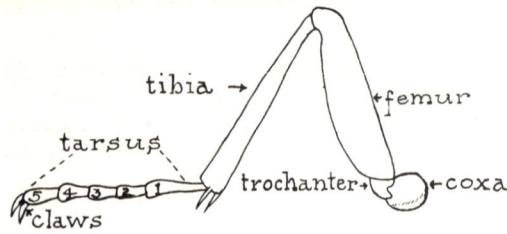

Figure 42. A typical insect leg showing the parts.

All insect legs have the same parts: A *coxa* that rotates in a cavity in the thorax, a *trochanter* (some insects have two trochanters on each leg), the *femur*, which is the largest segment of the leg, a usually long and slim *tibia*, and the *tarsus* or foot made up of two to five tarsal segments. The last tarsal segment usually bears a pair of claws. In counting tarsal segments, these claws should not be counted. The segments of all appendages are numbered from the attached end to the apical end.

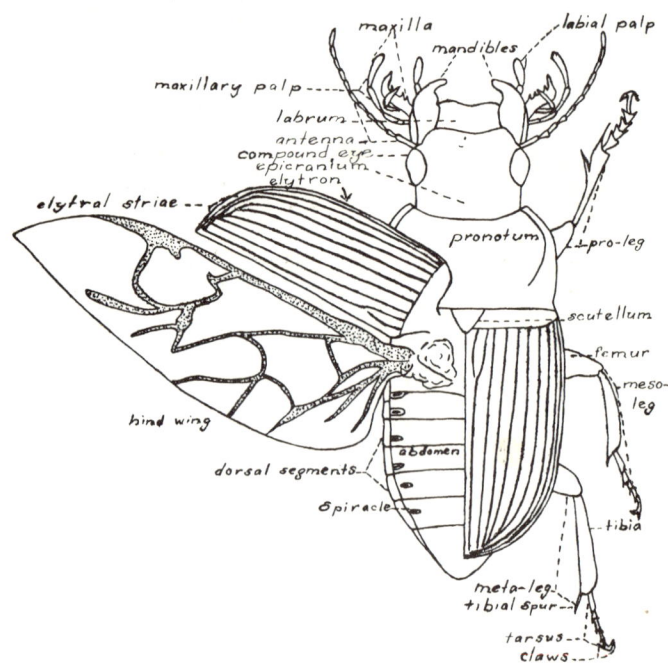

Figure 43. Dorsal view of a Beetle, **Harpalus caliginosus** (Fab.) showing parts.

The abdomen of insects is made of a number of horny rings which more or less telescope each other. These rings as well as those of the thorax, are in part punctured along each side by a row of openings (spiracles) through which the insect breathes. The end of the abdomen often bears parts having to do with mating and egg laying. The latter in the female are known as ovipositors and take various forms.

The upper part of an insect is its dorsal side; that below is the ventral side. The horny skeleton is arranged in plates (sclerites) all of which have names. Both a dorsal and a ventral view of a beetle are here shown, from which names and relationship of parts may be seen.

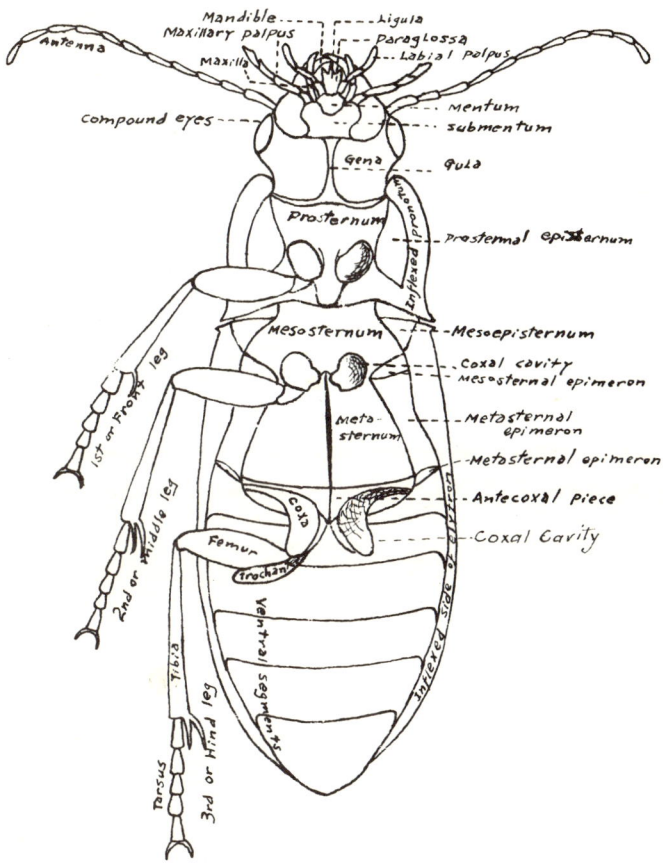

Figure 44. Ventral parts of an insect. (**Harpalus caliginosus** (Fab.)

SOME INSECT WINGS

In several orders of insects wing structures play an important part in identification. Typical wings of four of these orders are here pictured. The usual abbreviations have been employed in designating the veins as follows:—C, Costa; Sc, Subcosta; R, Radius; M, Medius; Cu, Cubitus; A, Anal. A cell is named from the vein bounding its upper side. The study of insect wings is a science in itself. Much has been written on the subject for those who wish to go into it further.

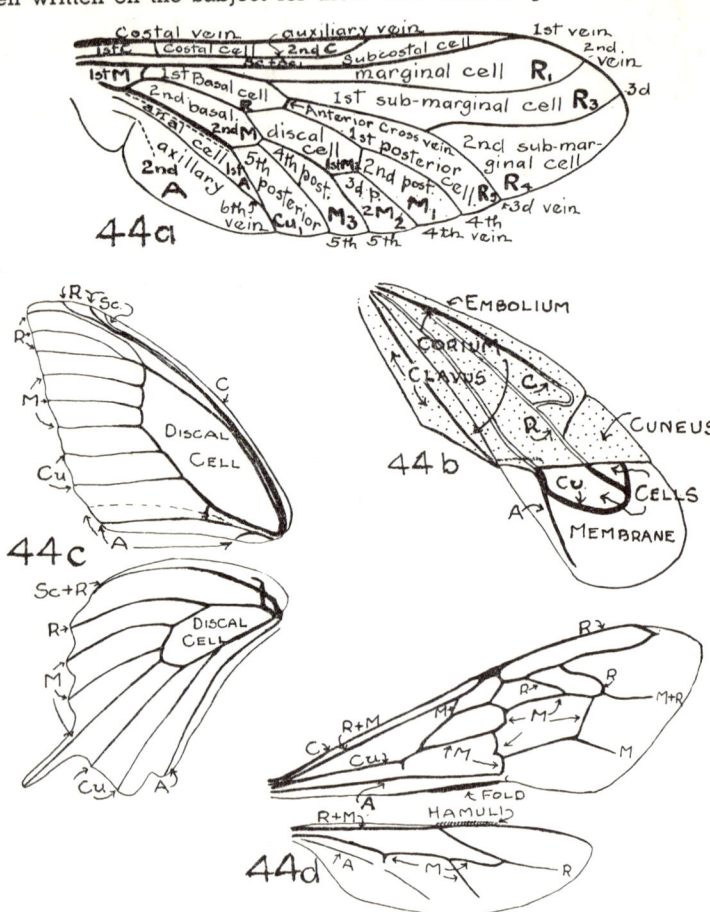

Figure 44a-d. Typical Insect Wings. 44a, Diptera (**Tabanus**) showing two methods of naming the cells and veins. 44b, Hemiptera, front wing (**Lygus**). 44c Lepidoptera, (**Papilio**). 44d, Hymenoptera, (**Apis**).

PICTURED-KEY TO THE ORDERS
OF INSECTS

1a Insects with wings. **2**
1b Insects having no wings or only inconspicuous vestiges of wings.**19**
2a Insects with only one pair of wings. **3**
2b Insects with two pairs of wings. Fig. 45. . . . .**5**

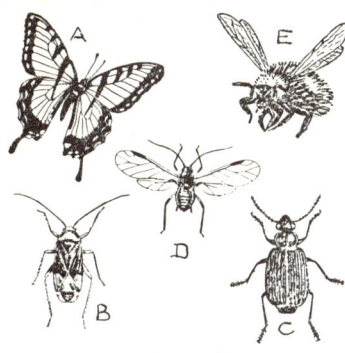

Figure 45

Fig. 45. Some typical four-winged insects. A, a Butterfly; B, a True Bug; C, a Ground Beetle; D, an Aphid; E, a Bee.

Almost all the winged insects except the True Flies have normally two pairs of wings. Several orders have occasional species with but one pair of wings. Many of the orders have some wingless species, or individuals with short flightless wings (brachypterous). For these latter species go to #19.

3a With one or more conspicuous filaments at end of abdomen; mouth parts poorly developed. **4**
3b Without filaments at end of abdomen; sucking, lapping or piercing mouth parts well developed. (Flies, mosquitos, etc.) Fig. 46.

Order XXIII, DÍPTERA page 139

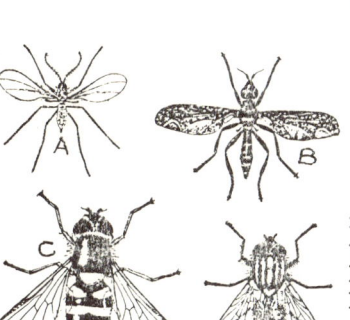

Figure 46

Fig. 46. Some Typical Flies.
A, The Wheat Midge, *Sitodíplosis mosellàna* (Gehin); B, a predacious fly, *Pyrgòta undàta* Wied.; C, a syrphid fly, *Sýrphus ribèsii* L.; D, The House Fly, *Musca domestica* L. (from U.S.D.A.)

The Diptera are the True Flies. They never have more than one pair of wings. Tiny knobbed structures known as balancers or halteres usually occur at the place of second wings. A few flies do not possess halteres and a few species are wholly wingless. Their young are usually legless and are called "wrigglers", "maggots" or "bots". The order is a large one, with many of its species not yet described.

**4a Wings slender, transparent with but one vein (usually two branch-
ed). Small halteres at place of second wing. (Male Scale Insects).
Fig. 47.**   **Order XVIII, HOMÓPTERA
Family 10, CÓCCIDAE**

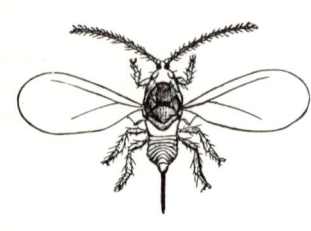

Figure 47

Fig. 47. Oystershell Scale (adult male)
Lepidosaphes úlmi (L.).

To the casual observer scale insects
are known only as incrustations or waxy
bodies on the stems, leaves and fruit of
plants. Many species are easily resog-
nized by the form of this scale covering. Both sexes have legs in their earlier instars. The females soon begin a
sedentary life under their protecting
scale with only their digestive and reproductive systems being highly functional. Only the adult males ever possess wings and some of them are wingless.

The males are short-lived and very
small. They will seldom come to the
attention of the beginner.

**4b Wings broad, with many veins; no halteres. (A few Mayflies).
Fig. 48.**   **Order IV. EPHEMERÓPTERA, page 67
Family 6, CAENIDAE**

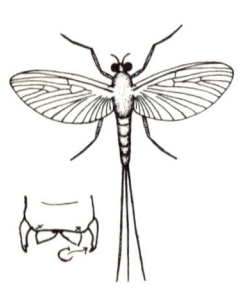

Figure 48

Fig. 48. A Two-winged Mayfly. *Caènis sp.*

The hind wings are much reduced in size
in all of the Mayflies. In the rather large
family *Caenidae* the hind wings are wholly
wanting. There are no wingless Mayflies and
only a few species of the family *Baetidae* in
addition to all of the *Caenidae* have but one
pair of wings.

The members of the *Caenidae* are small
in size and are often quite numerous. Their
wings are milky white and have comparatively few cross veins.

5a The two pairs of wings unlike in structure (the first pair thick and horny, as in the beetles (A); leathery at the base with overlapping membraneous tips, as in the true bugs (B) or leathery and with veins, as in the grasshoppers (C).) Fig. 49. 6

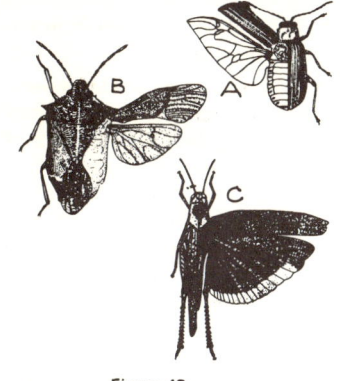

Figure 49

Fig. 49. Insects with front wings thicker than their back wings. A, a Leaf Beetle; B, a Stinkbug; C, a Grasshopper.

The elytra of beetles are not used for flight. They doubtless retard rather than aid their owners. The true bugs and the grasshoppers "flap" their front wings along with the hind ones.

Beginners should dissect a few of their specimens to be sure about these wing matters.

5b The two pairs of wings of similar structure and with about the same degree of thickness as in the bees, butterflies, dragonflies, etc.) (One pair is often colored and could thus differ from the other in transparency but not in thickness; or one or both may be covered with scales or hairs.) Fig. 50. 9

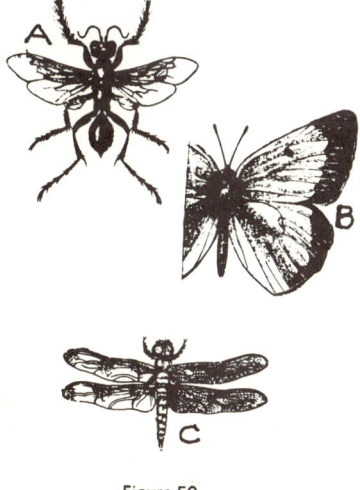

Figure 50

Fig. 50. Insects with wings of similar thickness. A, a Wasp; B, a Butterfly; C, a Dragonfly.

If one is to have a nice collection of insects he must resist all impulses to poke at or feel of specimens after they are mounted, —and to keep his friends from admiring them in that way, too. Dried specimens are entirely too fragile to survive such affectionate attention.

Beginners should find it profitable to make a secondary collection for "poking and feeling" purposes and use these specimens as roughly as necessary to determine their exact structure.

6a Outer (first) pair of wings of hard horn-like substance and meeting in a straight line down the back (as in the beetles and earwigs). Fig. 51. 7

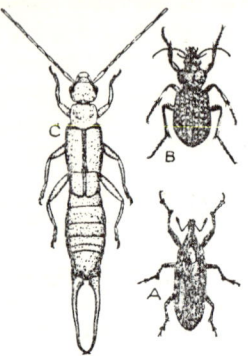

Figure 51

Fig. 51. Typical insects with horny wing covers which meet in a straight line. A, a Snout Beetle; B, a Ground Beetle; C, an Earwig.

Wing covers of this type are known as elytra and are made stiff and hard with chitin (kĭ-tin). There is almost always a pair of larger membraneous wings folded under them. A few flightless beetles and earwigs have no second pair of wings.

6b Wings not as in 6a. 8

7a With a prominent pair of pincer-like parts (A) at tip of abdomen. (Earwigs) Fig. 52. Order X, DERMÁPTERA, page 77

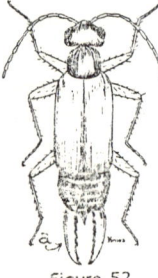

Figure 52

Fig. 52. An Earwig.

These peculiar insects are widely distributed though seldom seen in many temperate regions. They are active at night, often fly to lights, and are omnivorous in their food habits. Some species are beneficial in preying on harmful insects. Of course there is no foundation to the story of their entering the ears of man.

7b Without large pincers at the end of the abdomen. (Beetles). Fig. 53. Order XI, COLEÓPTERA, page 78

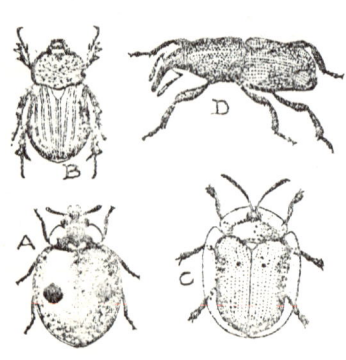

Figure 53

Fig. 53. Typical Beetles. A, *Adàlia bipunctàta* (L.).

The Two-spotted Ladybird (Family *Coccinéllidae*); B, *Euethèola rùgiceps* (Lec.) The Sugarcane Beetle (Family *Scarabaeidae*); C, *Metrìona bícolor* Fab. The Golden Tortoise Beetle (Family *Chrysomélidae*); D, *Sitóphilus orỳzae* (L.) The Rice Weevil (Family *Curculiónidae*).

This is the largest and likely the best known order of insects. Their structure, size and beauty make the beetles particularly attractive to amateur collectors.

8a (a, b, c) Front wings leathery at their base (A), membraneous and overlapping at their tips (B); mouth parts a tube for sucking (C), usually extending from underside of head in backward direction. (True Bugs). Fig. 54.

Order XVII. HEMÍPTERA page 106

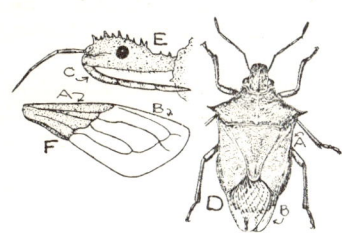

Figure 54

Fig. 54. D, A True Bug. *Pódisus maculivéntris* (Say). The Spined Soldier Bug (Family *Pentatómidae*); E, Head of a true bug (Family *Reduviidae*) showing sucking tube; F, Typical wing showing thick leathery base (A) and thinner membraneous tip (B). Family *Reduviidae*).

Hemiptera means "half wing". This peculiar wing condition and the sucking mouth parts make the members of this order very easy to recognize.

8b Front wings leathery, with veins: hind wings folded lengthwise when at rest. Mouth parts for chewing. (Crickets, Cockroaches, Katydids, Grasshoppers, etc.) Fig. 55.

Order VII. ORTHÓPTERA page 73

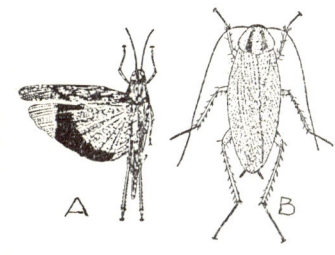

Figure 55

Fig. 55. Typical Orthóptera. A, *Trimerótropis marítima* (L.) The Beech Locust; B, *Periplanèta americàna* (L.) The American Cockroach.

This rather medium sized order is a very important one since it contains many highly destructive pests. Some systematists would split it into several orders since there is such radical differences in the different groups of insects it includes.

8c Front wings only slender club-like appendages; small to very small insects. (Twisted-winged Insects or Stylopids) Fig. 56.

Order XII. STREPSIPTERA

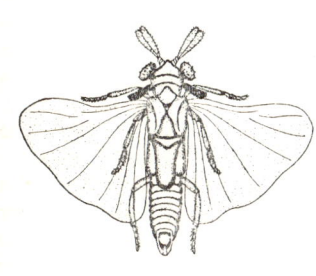

Figure 56

Fig. 56. A male *Stylópid*.

This is a small order of rather poorly known small to tiny insects. Many of them are parasitic on other insects, the females being larviform and never leaving their host, but may be seen when mature sticking out between the abdominal sclerites of their host. Other species live an independent life. The males of all species are winged and free-living.

9a Wings covered with scales (C) (in a few species there are bare transparent areas). Mouth parts a coiled tube for sucking. (Moths, Skippers and Butterflies) Fig. 57.

Order XXI, LEPIDOPTERA page 125

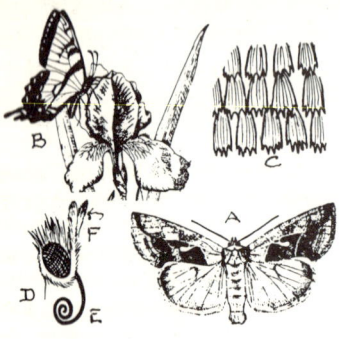

Figure 57

Fig. 57. A, *Anágrapha falcífera* (Kby.) The Celery Looper Moth; B, *Papílio gláucus túrnus* L. The Tiger Swallowtail; C, Scales enlarged; D, Head of butterfly showing coiled sucking tube (E) and palpi (F).

Scales characterize this order very much as feathers characterize birds. The broad wings (a few females have no wings) are usually "shingled" with beautiful designs in colored scales. For the most part, the adults are both handsome and harmless, but that does not free them with the jury. The children of many species have terrible ways as viewed by man, and year after year he pays heavily for their destructiveness. These caterpillars have three pairs of jointed legs and from two to five pairs of fleshy pro-legs.

9b Wings thin, not covered with scales, usually transparent or thinly clothed with hairs (sometimes colored) (as in Bees, Mayflies, Dragonflies, etc.). 10

10a Mouth parts a tube for sucking, attached to hinder part of the lower surface of the head. (E) Wings when at rest sloping down and outward from center thus ∧. (Cicadas, Leafhoppers, Treehoppers, Aphids, etc.). Fig. 58. Order XVIII, HOMÓPTERA page 117

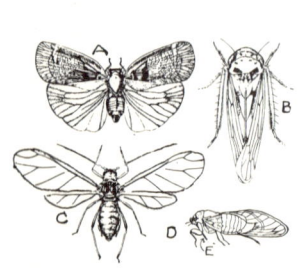

Figure 58

Fig. 58. Some typical Homoptera. A, *Órmenis pruinòsa* Say. (Family *Fulgóridae*); B, *Althýsanus exitiosus*. The Destructive Leafhopper (Family *Cicadéllidae*); C, *Toxóptera gráminum* (Rond.) The Greenbug (Family *Aphídidae*); D, *Magicicada septéndecim* (L.) The Periodical Cicàda (Family *Cicàdidae*).

The Homoptera are alike in that their membranous wings slope rooflike over the body. In size, shape, markings and habits they vary widely. They are vegetable feeders. Their sucking tube makes their feeding less conspicuous but the damage they do to plants is large.

10b Not as in 10a. **11**

11a Slender, moth-like insects, with long, slim antennae; no mouth-parts in evidence except a pair of slender palpi (a). Wings frequently hairy; usually broadest beyond the middle. (Caddis flies) Fig. 59. Order XX, TRICHÓPTERA page 124

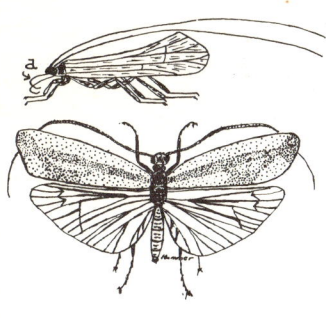

Figure 59

Fig. 59. *Limnéphilus rhómbicus* L.
Pale tan, front wings mottled with darker tan. Length about 15 mm.

These interesting insects are named and known best for their young. The larvae live in streams and build cases of web and little stones, twigs or debris, for their protection. They are so abundant that after the fish have eaten a large percentage of them, the adults developing from the remaining larvae become an intolerable nuisance at lights near water courses. Fishermen should be much interested in knowing more about these and our other aquatic insects, if fish culture is to be wholly successful.

11b Not as in 11a. **12**

12a Wings with but few cross veins (or none) as in the bees and thrips. Fig. 60. ....**13**

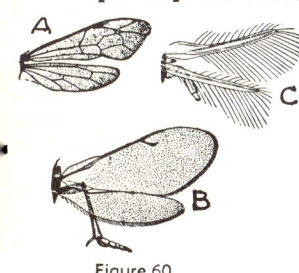

Figure 60

Fig. 60. A, Wings of an Ichneumon Wasp, *Pimpla conquisitor*; B, Wings of a Euphelmid wasp; C, wings of a Thrips.

Small wings usually make for rapid flight. The wings of the bees are generally fastened together by a series of hooklets so they may be operated as one. Hairs often provide most of the expanse in the wings of thrips.

12b Wings with several to many cross (vertical) veins, as in the dragonflies, lace wings, etc. Fig. 61. ....**14**

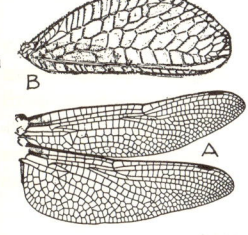

Figure 61

Fig. 61. Some many veined wings. A, *Dídymops sp.*, a Dragonfly; B, *Chrysòpa sp.*, a Lace Wing.

Six different orders have wings with numerous cross veins. For the most part their wings are large and they fly rather deliberately. The dragonflies are often swift and highly dexterous flyers.

13a Front wings the larger; hind wings frequently hooked to front wings. (Often mistaken for one pair by casual observers). Mouthparts for chewing or for both sucking and chewing. (Bees, wasps, ants). Fig. 62.   Order XXV. HYMENÓPTERA page 157

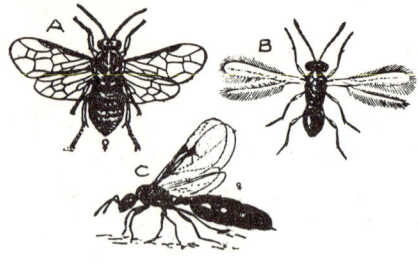

Figure 62

Fig. 62. Some typical *Hymenóptera;* A, *Pteronidea ribèsii* S., The Currant Worm; B, *Anaphoidea conotràcheli* Girt., The egg parasite of the plum curculio; C, *Monomòrium mínimum* (Buck.), The Little Black Ant.

From the viewpoint of social adjustments and intelligence, the Hymenoptera probably ranks the highest of any order of insects. It is a large order; some think that it will be found to contain more species than any other order of insects. Specimens should be mounted promptly when caught to keep them in good condition.

13b Very small, slender insects. Wings very narrow and margined with bristly hairs; mouthparts for piercing, chaffing and sucking. (Thrips) Fig. 63.   Order XIII. THYSANÓPTERA page 102

Figure 63

Fíg. 63. A Thrips (The plural and the singular are the same.) *Taeniothrips incónsequens* (Uzel). The Pear Thrips. (Family *Thrípidae).*

Thrips may be readily shaken from among the stamens of many flowers. They are also found on leaves, bulbs, roots, under loose bark and in drying fruit. The Giant Thrips of Australia becomes a half inch or more in length, but our species are tiny fellows ranging for the most part between one half and two mm. long.

14a Front wings much larger than hind wings. Wings when at rest held vertically above body. Two or three long fragile thread-like tails. (Outer two, "cerci"; all three, "caudal filaments".) (Mayflies) Fig. 64.   Order IV, **EPHEMEROPTERA** page 67

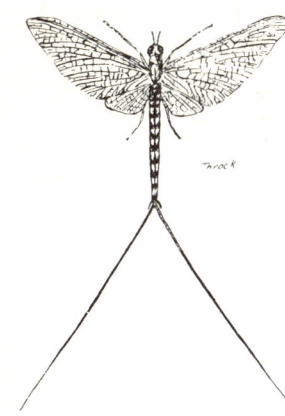

Figure 64

Fig. 64. *Hexagènia limbàta* Guerin.

Abdomen pale yellow, dorsal line and oblique lateral stripes dark. Length of body (without cerci) 15-22 mm.

The Mayflies are the only insects that molt after once getting their wings. Even then the adults live only a day or two. They appear in flight at lights in immense numbers at towns along rivers or lakes. Burlington, Iowa has an authentic record of a pile eight feet deep forming around an electric light pole one night when a heavy flight was in progress. Their nymphs are especially valuable as food for fish.

14b Not as in 14a. **15**

15a Head prolonged into a trunk-like beak with chewing mouth parts at its tip. (Scorpionflies) Fig. 65.

Order XXII, **MECÓPTERA** page 138

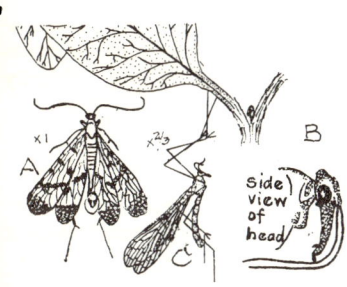

Figure 65

Fig. 65. A, *Panórpa sp.*, B, side view of head; C, *Bittacus sp.* (Family *Bittácidae)* awaiting its prey.

It is the turned up claspers on the end of the abdomen of the male of some species that give these insects the name Scorpionflies. Of course, they do not sting.

Several tiny wingless blackish species sometimes occur in great numbers in winter on snow. They belong to the family *Borèidae*.

15b Not as in 15a. **16**

16a Antennae short and inconspicuous; long slender insects with long narrow wings. (Damselflies, Dragonflies) Fig. 66.

Order V, ODONATA page 70

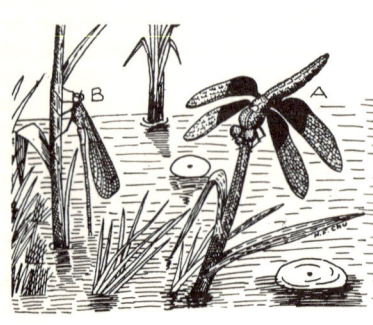

Figure 66

Fig. 66. A, a Dragonfly (family *Libellulidae*) at rest; B, a Damselfly (family *Coenagrionidae*) at rest.

The Dragonflies and Damselflies are always of interest. They have been given many popular names and a mass of superstition is built about them. They are wholly inoffensive to man. The adults live on mosquitos and other small insects taken from the air. The nymphs are ravenous highwaymen that waylay any creature of their own size that comes along in the water. Insects and young fish doubtless make up most of their food.

16b Antennae readily seen. **17**

17a Abdomen usually with two rather short tails (caudal cerci) (often extending beyond wing tips) (A). Back wings broader than front wings and folded length-wise (C). (Stoneflies). Fig. 67.

Order III, PLECOPTERA page 66

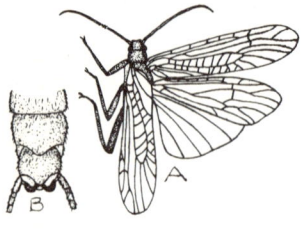

Figure 67

Fig. 67. A, a Stonefly; B, Tip of abdomen showing cerci.

Stoneflies are aquatic insects. The adults are often seen in rather large numbers flying at lights near watercourses on hot summer nights. A female may lay several thousand eggs. After the fish have eaten innumerable young stoneflies, enough of these immature forms (nymphs or naiads) survive to crawl out on the bank or up on logs and change to adults, to maintain a liberal balance.

17b Not as in 17a. **18**

18a Without caudal cerci (filaments at end of abdomen); (the males of some species have rather conspicuous claspers). Tarsi with five segments. (Antlions, Lacewings, Dobsonflies, Alderflies, Mantispids, etc.) Fig. 68. Order XIX, NEURÓPTERA page 121

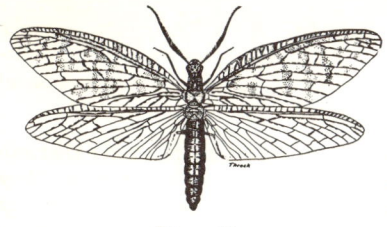

Figure 68

Fig. 68. *Chauliòdes rastricórnis* Ramb. (Family *Siálidae*).

In the earlier days of entomology this order included many insects now placed in separate orders. Many systematists would divide the group still further. Its members are interesting but for the most part not highly economic.

18b Wings equal in size and with indistinct veins. Prothorax smaller than head. (Termites or White Ants) Fig. 69. Order IX, ISÓPTERA

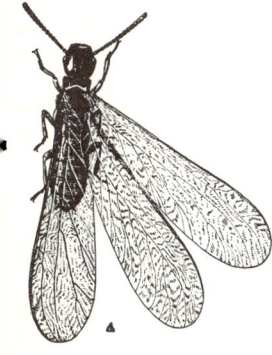

Figure 69

Fig. 69. A White Ant. (Queen) *Reticulitérmes flàvipes* Kollar. The Common Northern Termite. (U. S. D. A.)

Males and queens at swarming time winged and dark brown or black. Wings are broken off when a "Royal pair" establishes their colony. Workers, soldiers, and nymphs wingless, white. See Fig. 73.

In our region Termites are sometimes found in decaying logs in the woods where they are of little consequence. Sometimes they invade cities and do serious damage to the buildings. Unlike the true ants, both sexes are represented among the workers. They have a highly organized communal life.

19a With balancers (halteres) on the thorax. (Rarely absent) (Wingless Flies) Fig. 70. Order XXIII, DÍPTERA page 139

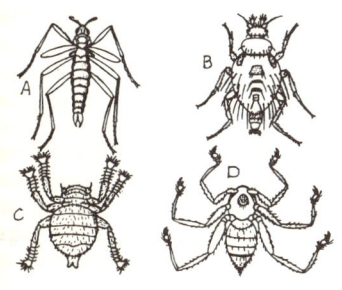

Figure 70

Fig. 70. Some Wingless Flies. A, *Eretmóptera* sp. (family *Chironómidae*); B, *Ecitomỳia* sp., (family *Phóridae*); C, *Braùla càeca* Nitzsch, the Honey-bee Parasite, (family *Braúlidae*); D, *Basília* sp., a spider-like fly parasitic on bats, (family *Nycteribìidae*).

Curran lists 16 families of Diptera which contain some species having no wings or only aborted wings. The four species here pictured are redrawn from his North American Diptera.

19b Without balancers on the thorax. **20**

20a Narrow waisted ant-like insects; no caudal cerci. (Ants, **Velvet Ants,** etc.) Fig. 71.   Order XXV, HYMENOPTERA page 157

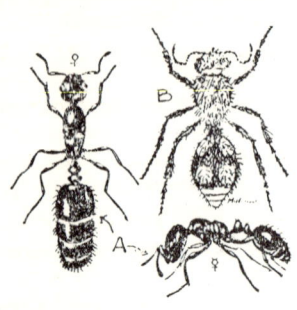

Figure 71

Fig. 71. A, *Monomòrium mínimum*(Buck.) The Little Black Ant (family *Formícidae)*; B, *Dasymútilla intérrupta* Banks, a common Velvet Ant, (family *Mutílidae).*

Several families of Hymenoptera have some wingless species. In a few instances both sexes are always wingless, but with most species, the worker females are the ones which lack wings. Queen ants after making their nuptial flight and establishing their colony break off their wings. This was likely the earliest form of one "burning his bridges behind him.".

20b Not narrow waisted as in 20a. **21**

21a Head prolonged into a trunk-like beak with chewing mouth parts. (Snow Scorpionflies and others) Fig. 72.

Order XXII, MECÓPTERA page 138

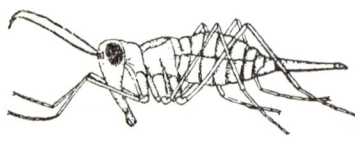

Figure 72

Fig. 72. A Snow Scorpionfly, *Bòreus califórnicus* Packard, (family *Borèidae).*

Both the larvae and the adults of these small insects (2.5-3 mm.) may be found in forest debris and mosses in favorable regions throughout the year, but it is when the leaping adults appear in large numbers on the snow that they attract the most attention. The family *Bittácidae* also has some wingless species.

21b Head not prolonged into a beak as in 21a. **22**

22a Ant-like but with wide waist and two short caudal cerci. Not flattened. Usually light colored. (White Ants or Termites) Fig. 73.

Order IX, ISÓPTERA

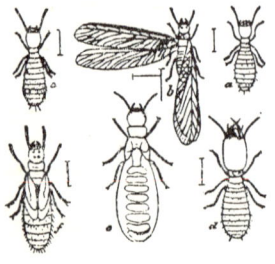

Figure 73

Fig. 73. White Ants. (a Worker, b Male, c, e, f Stages of Females, d Soldier. *Reticulitérmes flàvipes* Kollar. The Common Northern Termite. (from U. S. D. A.)

Soft bodied, wingless, whitish. They live within their tunnels in wood and seldom if ever appear at the surface. Length 5-7 mm. They are exceedingly destructive.

22b Not as in 22a. 23

23a Small, flat bodied insects with head as wide as body or nearly so. Chewing mouthparts. 24

23b Not as in 23a. 25

24a Antennae of many segments. Found on old papers, etc. (Book
Lice, Bark Lice, Psocids) Fig. 74.

Order XIV, CORRODÉNTIA page 103

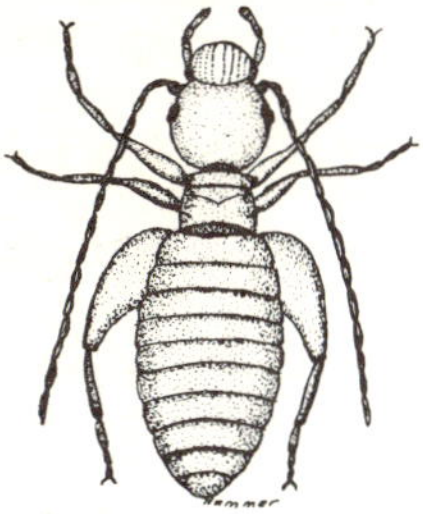

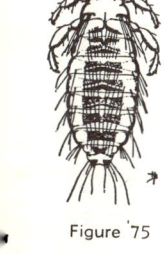

Fig. 74. A book Louse. *Lipóscelis divanatòrius*
Mull.

Grayish white; eyes dark. Length about 1
mm. It is known also as the Death Watch on account of the ticking noise it makes.

Some members of this order have two pairs
of wings, and resemble aphids. They are known
as barklice and are found on tree trunks, on
Figure 74   dead leaves, in lichens, etc.

24b Antennae short; two to five segments. Found mostly on birds, a
few on mammals. (Bird Lice) Fig. 75.

Order XV, MALLÓPHAGA page 104

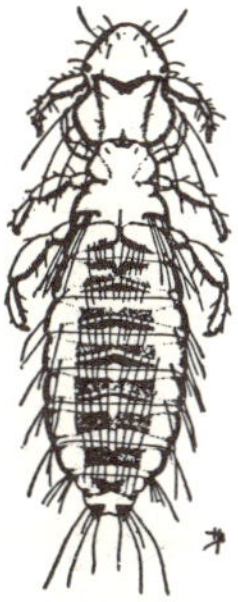

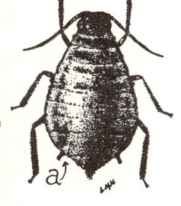

Fig. 75. A Bird Louse. *Lipeùrus heterógraphus* Nitzsch.
The Chicken Head Louse.
Pale to dark gray. Much flattened. Feed on skin
scales of young chickens and turkeys. Length 2-3 mm.
(from U. S. D. A.)
This order includes many species, most of which
are parasites on birds. There are probably as many
species as there are species of birds. A few species
of biting lice live on domestic mammals. They do
not eat the flesh of their host but are very annoying
Figure 75   and may even cause death.

25a Small, soft-bodied insects with small heads and plump bodies.
Two short tubes usually extending from back of abdomen (a).
Found sucking juice from plants. Frequently attended by ants.
(Plant Lice or Aphids) Fig. 76.

Order XVIII, HOMÓPTERA page 117

Fig. 76. An Aphid. *Àphis màidi-rádicis* Forbes. The
Corn root Aphid.
Whitish. Found on roots of corn where it is placed
and cared for by ants (See Fig. 54). All summer long
there are many generations of nothing but females
which produce living young. At the approach of cold
weather males and egg laying females are formed.
The ants care for the eggs during the winter and see
Figure 76   that the young find proper food when they hatch in
the spring. Length about 2 mm. (from U. S. D. A.)

25b Not as in 25a. **26**

26a Small, broad and flat across back; fleshy legs, each with single hook like claw for grasping hairs; fleshy, unjointed, sucking beak. Found on mammals. (Sucking Lice.) Fig. 77.

Order XVI, ANOPLURA page 105

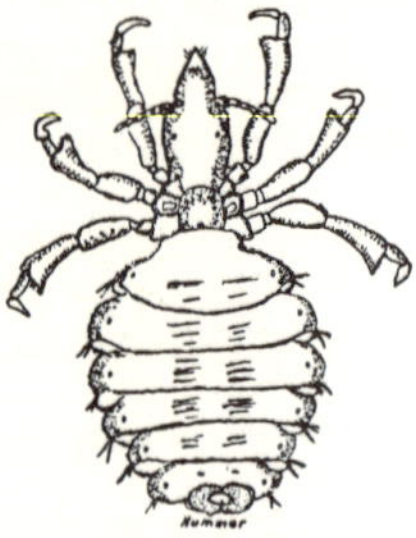

Fig. 77. A Sucking Louse. *Haematópinus adventícius* Neum. The Hog Louse.

Grayish brown with black markings. Lives by sucking the blood of the hog. Length 4-6 mm.

The true lice are confined in their hosts to the mammals. Two species prey on man, while cattle, the horse, sheep, dog and several wild mammals each have at least one species. Some groups of mammals seem to be practically immune from attacks of True Lice.

Figure 77

26b Not as in 26a. **27**

27a Small narrow insects, flattened on the sides; sucking mouthparts; hind legs for jumping; five tarsal segments. (Fleas) Fig. 78.

Order XXIV, SIPHONÁPTERA page 156

Fig. 78. The Dog Flea. *Ctenocéphalis cànis* Curtis.

Reddish brown. Infests dog, cat and man. Length 3-5 mm. (from U. S. D. A.)

Fleas parasitize both the mammals and birds and live by sucking the blood of their host. The larvae are worm-like and live on decaying organic matter.

Figure 78

27b Not as in 27a. **28**

28a Body thickly covered with scales, mouthparts for sucking or absent. (A few female moths) Fig. 79.

Order XXI, LEPIDÓPTERA page 125

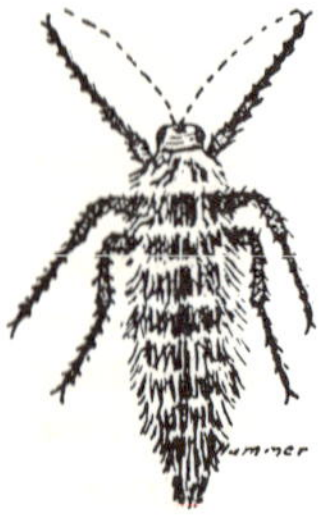

Fig. 79. The Spring Cankerworm, (female) *Paleácrita vernàta* Peck.

Gray, covered with scales. Appear from February to April. Length 10-15 mm.

Relatively few *Lepidoptera* are flightless. The families *Arctiidae*, *Lymantriidae*, *Geométridae*, *Psýchidae* and *Tortrícidae* each have a few females which are wingless or have only rudimentary wings.

Figure 79

28b Not as in 28a. **29**

29a Very delicate insects with chewing mouthparts and long, jointed thread-like tails and antennae. (Fishmoths, Bristletails, Firebrats). Fig. 80.
Order I, THYSANURA page 64

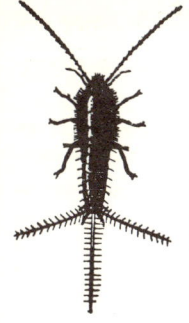

Fig. 80. The Silverfish. *Lepísma sacchárina* L.

Light silvery gray. Soft body, flattened. Runs rapidly. Length about 13 mm. (from U. S. D. A.)

The members of this order are widely distributed throughout the world. Many species live on or in the ground and are seldom noticed. Others invade our homes and become pests.

Figure 80

29b Not as in 29a. **30**

30a Mouth parts for biting and chewing (possessing mandibles). ..**31**

30b Mouth parts for piercing and sucking. **34**

31a Delicate insects with six or fewer abdominal segments. Underside of abdomen has a sucker (D) and a pair of more or less fused appendages (C) for leaping (furculum). (Springtails) Fig. 81.
Order II, COLLEMBOLA page 65

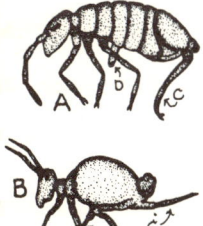

Fig. 81. Typical Springtails. A, *Entomòbrya* sp., (family *Entomobrýidae*); B, *Smynthùrus* sp., (family *Smynthùridae*); C, furcula; D, ventral sucker or tube (tenaculum).

These tiny creatures appear in unusual places and at times in almost unbelievable numbers. A plowed field was called to our attention early one spring where a common species had congregated in dozens of round-topped piles, each containing a half bushel or more of these drab colored little fellows, each pile containing more individuals than there are people in New York City.

Figure 81

31b Not as in 31a. **32**

32a Very minute, slender, white "insects" having neither eyes or antennae in evidence. Front legs held erect like antennae; first three of the twelve abdominal segments bear short appendages. (Proturans) Fig. 82. Order 0, PROTURA

Fig. 82. *Eoséntomon* sp. (after Berlese).

These very tiny little animals have come into the entomological picture in comparatively recent years. They live in damp places under leaves, rock, etc. Not much is known about their way of living. A tiny spot on each side of the head seems to be the vestige of an antenna.

They use only their middle and hind legs for walking. Less than a hundred species have been described.

Figure 82

32b Not as in 32a. 33

33a (a, b, c) Antennae thread like; face directed forward or downward. (Crickets, roaches, grasshoppers, walkingsticks) Fig. 83.

Order VII, ORTHÓPTERA page 73

Fig. 83. *Ceuthóphilus maculàtus* (Harris) Spotted Camel Cricket. (family *Tettigonìidae*).

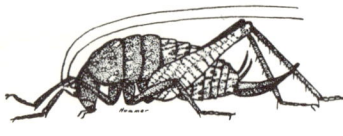

Brown, often with median lighter stripe on thorax. Several yellowish spots on dorsal surface of abdomen. Length 14-19 mm.

Figure 83

While most of the Orthoptera are winged, each of the orders have at least a few species which have been denied organs of flight. They have chewing mouthparts, are herbivorour or omnivorous in their feeding habits and often do serious damage.

33b Antennae bead-like, club-like or comb-like, but without prominent forceps at tip of abdomen. (Beetles) Fig. 84.

Order XI, COLEÓPTERA page 78

Fig. 84.

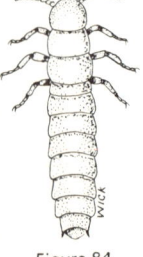

The females of some beetles are larviform; (i. e. they never look like adults) and, of course have no wings. Other species may be devoid of both elytra and wings while a considerable number of species possess elytra, but no wings and are flightless.

Figure 84

33c With prominent pair of movable forceps at tip of abdomen. (Ear-wigs) Fig. 85.   **Order X, DERMÁPTERA page 77**

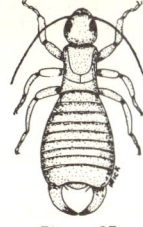

Figure 85

Fig. 85. *Esphálmenus* sp.

A few genera of earwigs like the one pictured have neither elytra nor membraneous wings. Others have elytra of varying length but possess no flying wings.

34a Small legless insects firmly attached to plant leaves or stems. Frequently covered with a waxy scale. (Scale insects) Fig. 86.   **Order XVIII, HOMÓPTERA page 117**

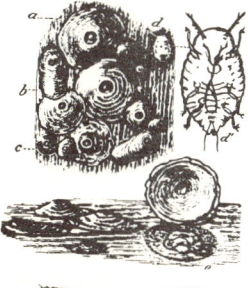

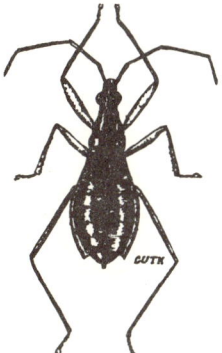

Figure 86

Fig. 86. The San Jose Scale. (a, c, d and e, females; b and g males) *Aspidiòtus perniciòsus* Comst.

Female scale round, gray, with raised center reddish yellow. Diameter about 2 mm. Male scale black oblong, about 1 mm. long. Mature female insect yellowish, wingless, legless, does not leave scale, but gives birth to living young. Male adult yellow, two-winged, active. (From U. S. D. A.)

These rather insonspicuous insects are exceedingly destructive especially to fruit and to green house plants. They are cosmopolitan in their distribution. A few species furnish valuable commercial products such as cochineal, shellac, etc.

34b Well developed legs; sucking beak arising at front of head and held between the legs. (True bugs) Fig. 87.   **Order XVII, HEMÍPTERA page 106**

Figure 87

Fig. 87. *Nàbis subcoleoptràtus* Kby.

Subdepressed. Shiny jet black. Edge of abdomen and legs yellowish. Wings very short. A fully winged form occurs, but is rare. Length 9-12 mm.

Not only this family (Nábidae) but the Cimícidae, Lygèidae and Gérridae also contain some flightless forms of Hemiptera. In some cases both winged and "wingless" forms occur in the same species.

ORDER THYSANÙRA

1a Body with covering of scales; three appendages behind (long median filament between two cerci). (Bristletails) 2

1b Body naked; with a pair of long cerci but no mid-filament behind. (Campodeids) Fig. 88.   Family 3, CAMPODEIDAE

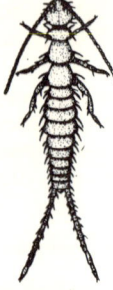

Fig. 88. *Campòdea folsòmi* Silv.

These slender usually white, fragile little insects live in vegetable litter, under rocks and logs and in other damp secluded places. They are not known to have any economic importance. They can be easily reared in small enclosures if sufficient humidity is maintained. They have no eyes.

Figure 88

2a Eyes large and united or touching each other; two ocelli; tarsi with three segments. (Machilids) Fig. 89.   Family 1, MACHILIDAE

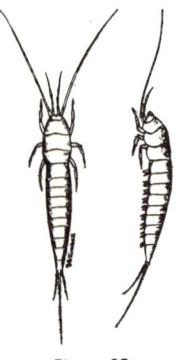

Fig. 89. *Màchilis variàbilis* Say (Kan. S.B.A.).

The some 150 members of this family have not invaded the haunts of man but live out of doors sheltered by the plants and debris of woods and open fields. They are ordinarily of sluggish movements but are good jumpers when the occasion requires. The seven segmented maxillary palpi are often longer than the legs. The larger species attain a body length of 15 or more mm. They are cosmopolitan but most frequent in the tropics.

Figure 89

2b Eyes widely separated and small, or none; no ocelli; tarsi with three or four segments. (Bristletails, Silverfish, Slickers) Fig. 90.
          Family 2, LEPISMIDAE

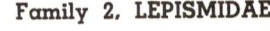

Fig. 90. *Thermòbia doméstica* (Pack.) The Fire Brat.

Soft fragile body covered with silvery gray scales with mottled dark markings above. 12-15 mm. Frequents places where starchy foods may be had. Often very common at night.

The family has more than 200 species and is cosmopolitan in its distribution.

Figure 90

ORDER COLLEMBOLA

1a Body somewhat spherical in shape; head vertical; antennae longer than the head. Fig. 91. Family 4, SMYNTHURIDAE

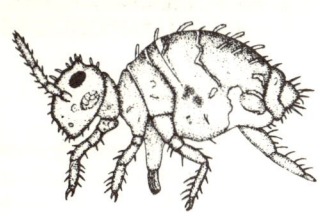

Figure 91

Fig. 91. *Neosminthurus curvisetis* (Guthrie)

Bluish brown to light brown. Length 1 mm. Rather common in humus and moss.

The some 50 North American members of this family are rather spherical, odd looking creatures. They are usually found in wet places and are plant feeders.

1b Body more elongate; head horizontal; furcula sometimes obscure..2

2a Prothorax normal, seen from above, top clothed with bristles; antennae with but four segments; furcula sometimes absent. (Springtails, Snowfleas) Fig. 92. Family 1, PODURIDAE

Figure 92

Fig. 92. *Achorutes armatus* Nicolet.

Dark blue to bright yellow with widely varying patterns of spots and streaks. Eight eyes on each side of head; furcula well developed; anal horns two.

This cosmopolitan species is very common. Look for it in soil, decaying leaves, etc.

Over 50 North American species have been named for the family. Several "snowfleas" and the very common Water Springtail belong here.

2b Prothorax naked above; membranous; largely covered by the mesonotum; antennae with four to six segments; furcula almost always present. Fig. 93. Family 2, ENTOMOBRYIDAE

Figure 93

Fig. 93. *Folsomia elongata* (MacG.)

Gray to dark brown. Eyes eight on each side. Antennae about equal to head. Furcula reaching posterior margin of second abdominal segment. Length up to 1.5 mm. Very common and widely distributed.

About 100 North American species are known for this most important family of the Collembola. The body is usually cylindrical and the furcula long.

ORDER PLECÓPTERA

1a Front wing with at most only one row of crossveins in anal area, often none. Front coxae separated. 2

1b Two or more rows of crossveins in anal area of front wing. Front coxae close together. Fig. 94.   Family 1, PTERONARCIDAE

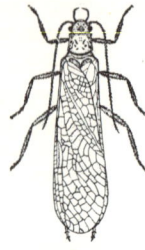

Figure 94

Fig. 94. *Pteronárcys dorsàta* Say. The Giant Stone-fly.

Dark brown, paler below; abdomen pale yellow on under side; veins of wings blackish. This is our largest known stonefly. Length to tip of wing 40 to 60 mm.

Almost all the species in this rather small family are of large size. The wings are usually clouded. The members of the family are widely distributed.

2a Cerci with many segments, long. 3

2b Cerci short with but one to a few segments (never more than ten); last vein in front wing branching after it leaves the anal cell. (Threadtailed Stoneflies) Fig. 95.   Family 3, NEMOURIDAE

Figure 95

Fig. 95. *Nemoùra vallicúlaris* Wu.

Blackish brown; antennae dark brown; wings smoky; legs yellowish brown. Length to tip of wing 11 to 13 mm.

The short tails characterize this family. The species are mostly dark colored. This large family has wide distribution.

3a Several crossveins in front wing connecting the medius and the cubital veins (A). Fig. 96.   Family 2, PÉRLIDAE

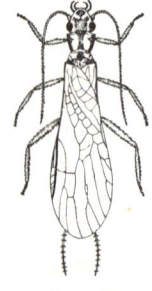

Figure 96

Fig. 96. *Perlínella drỳmo* Newm.

General color brown; head and pronotum yellow marked with black as pictured; antennae and legs dark. Length to tip of wing 11 to 19 mm.

This large family includes many of the best known stoneflies. Some of the larger species are dark in color but the smaller species, of which there are many, are usually greenish or yellowish. A few males have shortened wings.

3b With not more than two or three crossveins in front wing connecting the Medius and the cubital veins (A); both anal veins unbranched. (Smoky Stoneflies) Fig. 97.   **Family 4, CAPNIIDAE**

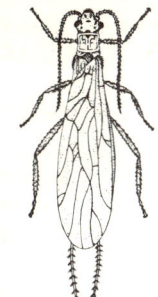

Fig. 97. *Capnella pygmaea* Burm.

Blackish or dark brown; legs brown; wings of male not reaching the tip of abdomen. Length 3-7 mm.

The smallest known stoneflies belong to this family. They seldom exceed 12 mm. in length. The total number of known species is not large.

Figure 97

ORDER EPHEMEROPTERA

1a With two pairs of wings. (a few exceptions) 2

1b With but one pair of wings which are usually whitish and ciliated behind. Small insects. Wings with few cross veins; caudal filiments three; claspers of male (C) usually with but one segment. Fig. 98.   **Family 6, CAENIDAE**

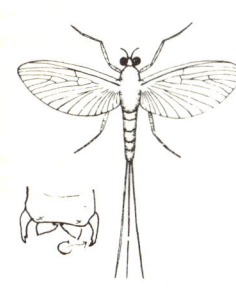

Fig. 98. *Caenis* sp. C, ventral view of tip of abdomen showing claspers of male.

This family is a large one and widely distributed. The tiny, milky winged little adults occasionally appear in great number along water courses on hot nights. The second pair of gills of the naiads is very large. Both adults and young are small and fragile.

These tiny little fellows are not often out, but when they do appear they usually come in great numbers. They are so delicate that the collector must use extraordinary care in handling them.

Figure 98

2a Hind tarsi with not over 4 movable segments. (a fifth is occasionally in evidence but is rigidly fused with the tibia. 3

2b Hind tarsi with 5 movable segments. Front wings with many veins; hind wings oval; caudal filaments 2; claspers of male with 4 segments. Fig. 99. Family 10, SIPHLONURIDAE

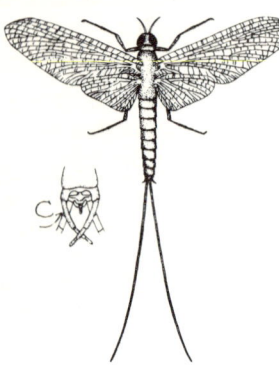

Figure 99

Fig. 99. *Chirotónetus* sp. C, tip of abdomen, top view, showing claspers of male.

Representatives of this fairly large family are found on all continents. The naiads live in running water and have small heads and flat gills.

Much is said and written about the short life of Mayflies, but that is true only of the adults. They emerge at sundown as sub-adults with wings and then rather shortly molt again to become fully adult and in a few hours lay their eggs and die. Their adult life span at most is a matter of only a few days but their entire life, naiad and adult may be a matter of months or even a few years.

3a Veins M and Cu of front wing strongly divergent; caudal filaments 2 or 3; claspers of male with 4 segments, the second being the longer. Fig. 100. Family 2, EPHEMERIDAE

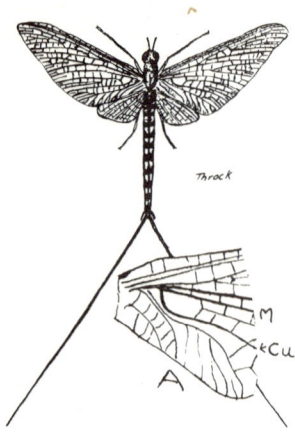

Figure 100

Fig. 100. *Hexagènia limbàta* Guerin. A, base of front wing enlarged. Pale yellow with brownish stripes. Length of body alone 15-22 mm.

This family contains some of our most abundant Mayflies. They often appear in immense numbers on warm nights along large bodies of water, and become a serious but not dangerous nuisance on show windows and at street lights.

The naiads dig in the mud; they taper at both ends and have sharp mandibles.

3b Veins M and Cu parallel at base or nearly so. (See Fig. 101A) ..4

4a Vein M of front wing not forked; front wings with fewer cross veins; hind wings small and narrow (occasionally absent); caudal filaments two; claspers with 4 segments but seemingly only three. Fig. 101. Family 5, BAETIDAE

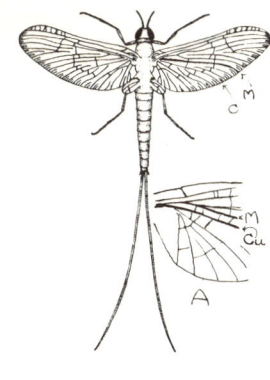

Figure 101

Fig. 101. *Baètis* sp. A, base of front wing enlarged; M, medius; C, cubitus.

Here is another large family of widely scattered species, many of which at times show up in great abundance. The naiads have long legs and antennae. In choice of feeding ground some live in quiet water while others hunt out the rapids or waterfalls.

The species *posticatus* is one of the most abundant Mayflies on the upper Mississippi. The life cycle is apparently a little less than a year and is characterized by more than 20 moults.

4b Vein M of front wing forked; hind wings small; caudal filaments 3; claspers of male with 3 or 4 segments, the second one long and incurved. Fig. 101½. Family 7, LEPTOPHLEBIIDAE

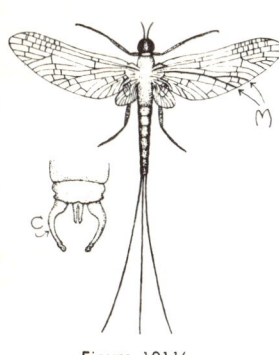

Figure 101½

Fig. 101½. *Chorotérpes* sp. C, tip of abdomen with claspers; M, median vein (branched).

The members of this rather large family are widely distributed. The many fine cross veins make them readily distinguished from the preceding family. The naiads have a variation of tastes in selecting their living places. They may often be found under stones.

ORDER ODONÀTA

1a Hind wings wider than front wings near base. When at rest wings extended on either side at right angles to the body. Strong flyers. (Dragonflies) Fig. 102. 3

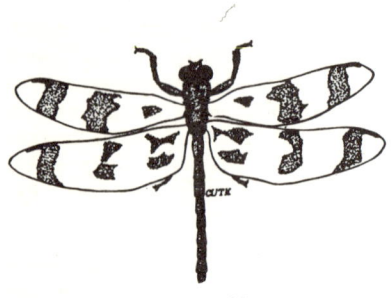

Figure 102

Fig. 102. *Celíthemis eponína* Drury. (Family *Libellùlidae).*

Wings yellowish, marked with brown. Face yellow; thorax brown with blackish stripes; abdomen black, streaked with yellow. Length 40 mm. Expanse 70 mm.

The Dragonflies are much more sturdily built than the Damselflies and will average considerably larger. Large damselflies, however, are larger than some small species of dragonflies. The dragonflies are strong flyers and some species fly at considerable height and with great speed. Feeding, mating, egg-laying, — in fact most of their daylight life — is spent on the wing. They are quick to detect movements. When one strikes at them with a net and misses they frequently return to see what it was all about with the result that many a fine specimen graces a collection that would not otherwise be there. At night they roost in tall grasses, shrubs and weeds, and may be easily collected.

1b Front and hind wings similar in size and shape. When at rest wings folded together edge up, parallel to the body. Feeble flyers. (Damselflies) Fig. 103. 2

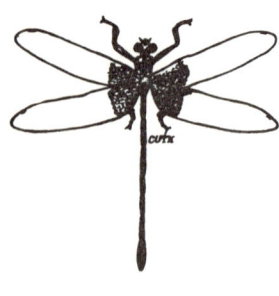

Figure 103

Fig. 103. *Hetaerìna americána* (Fabr.)

The Common Ruby Spot. (family *Agrionidae).*

Thorax bronze; abdomen greenish bronze. Spots at base of wings ruby-red in male; amber-yellow in female. Length 44 mm. Expanse 58 mm.

The Damselflies seem to live a life of leisure as compared to the hustling dragonflies. They are for the most part low feeble flyers. The immature members (nymphs or naiads), as with the dragonflies, live in water and are predacious. Damselfly naiads may be recognized by the three leaf-like tracheal gills at the posterior end of the body.

ODONATA

2a Wings with five or more antenodal cross veins (A). Wings not narrowed to form a stalk at base. (The Broad-winged Damselflies.) Fig. 104.

Family 3, AGRIONIDAE

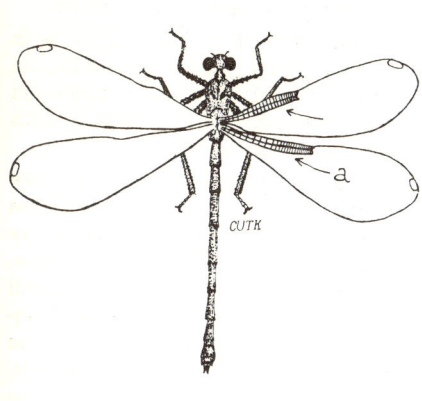

Figure 104

Fig. 104. *Ágrion maculátum* Beauv.

Entire body brilliant metallic green, wings wholly black in male. The female has a white stigma on wings and colors are paler. A most beautiful and exceedingly interesting damselfly. Length 42 mm. Expanse 64 mm.

This little family contains two groups of delightfully charming damselflies, — the "Black Wings" and the "Ruby Spots." Brilliant metallic colored bodies with blackened wings characterize the one while the other displays bronze bodies with red spotted wings in the males. (See Fig. 103).

2b Wings with only two or three antenodal cross veins (A). Wings narrowed to form a stalk at base (B). (The Narrow-winged Damselflies) Fig. 105.

Family 4, COENAGRIÓNIDAE

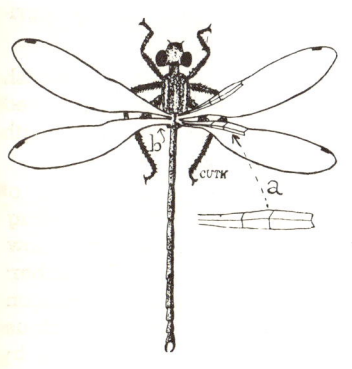

Figure 105

Fig. 105. *Léstes uncàtus* Kirby

Metallic green; sides of body yellow. Legs blackish, lined with yellow; tarsi black. Length 40 mm. Expanse 42 mm.

Most of our species of damselflies belong in this family. They are abundant along all permanent water courses. They are mostly clear winged but their bodies are beautifully marked with delicate shades of blue, green, tan and red, and with black.

3a Antenodal cross veins in first and second row not meeting each other (A). Triangles in fore and hind wing similar in shape and relative position. Fig. 106.　　　　　　Family 1, AESCHNIDAE

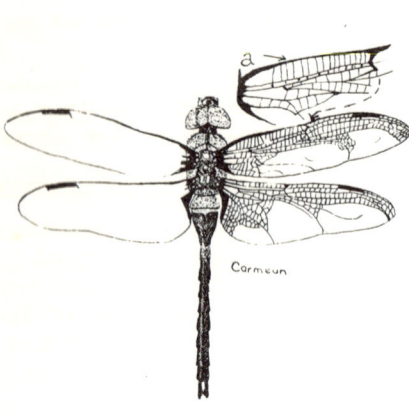

Figure 106

Fig. 106. Ànax jùnius (Drury)

Thorax green, abdomen bluish. Femora reddish; remainder of legs blackish. Wings transparent with amber sheen. Length 76 mm. Expanse 104 mm.

This family includes our largest and swiftest flying dragonflies. They are often seen long distances from water. Mosquitos, moths, and many other flying insects make up their diet, which they tear apart and eat with their large jaws. In some regions they have proven a pest to bee raisers by destroying large numbers of honey bees.

3b Antenodal cross veins in second row a continuation of those in the first row (A). Triangles in fore and hind wing unlike in shape and differently placed. (The Skimmers.) Fig. 107.
　　　　　　　　　　　　Family 2, LIBELLULIDAE

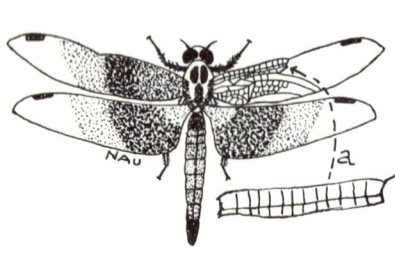

Figure 107

Fig. 107. Libéllula lactùosa Burm. The Widow.

Abdomen blackish, striped with yellow; legs dark. Base of wings marked with brown. A common species. Length 47 mm. Expanse 84 mm.

This family of dragonflies is considerably larger than the preceding in number of species. They cover a rather wide range in size and show many brilliant colors with frequently different patterns for the two sexes. The abdomen is usually shorter and proportionately heavier than in the Aeschnidae.

ORDER ORTHOPTERA

1a Hind legs for leaping. Three or four tarsal segments. (See Figs. 108-112) **2**

1b Hind legs not fitted for leaping. Five tarsal segments. (See Figs. 113-115). **6**

2a Three tarsal segments. (Sometimes apparently 2 on first and second legs). **3**

2b Four tarsal segments (rather rarely less); ovipositor of females usually conspicuous, sword-shaped or sickle-shaped; auditory organ, if possessed, near base of front tibia. (Long-horned Grasshoppers, Katydids, Camel Crickets) Fig. 108.

Family 6, TETTIGONIIDAE

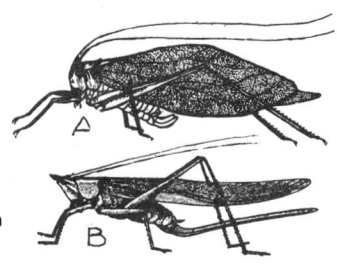

Figure 108

Fig. 108. A, *Microcéntrum rhombifòlium* (Saussure). Broad-winged Katydid. Grass green. Length of body 25-30 mm.

B, *Neoconocéphalus ensíger* (Harris). The Swordbearer. Green. Length of body ♂ 24-26 mm. ♀ (including ovipositor) 55-65 mm.

The Katydids and meadow grasshoppers belong here. They are usually green and the female has a sword-like ovipositor. The camel crickets, queerly shaped, humpbacked wingless forms that live in dark places, are also included in the family. They range from a mottled light brown to dark brown in color. (See Fig. 83).

3a Antennae short. **4**

3b Antennae long and slender. Ovipositor slender, nearly cylindrical, usually long (shorter in the Tree Crickets). (Field Crickets, Tree Crickets, Bush Crickets Fig. 109.   Family 8, GRYLLIDAE

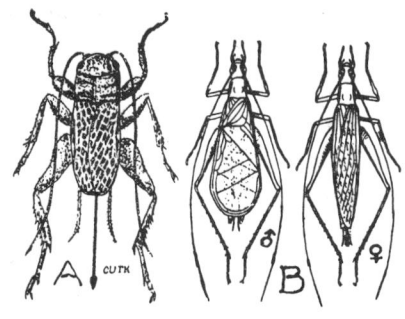

Figure 109

Fig. 109. A, *Grýllus assímilis* Fab. The Common Field Cricket. Black or dark brown. Length 14-25 mm. B, *Oecanthus niveus* DeG. The Snowy Tree Cricket. Pale green or white. Length 12-15 mm. (After Fulton).

There are a number of subfamilies of crickets differing in structure and habits. The sword bearing crickets, bush crickets, tree crickets, field crickets and tiny little crickets that live with the ants. They are all largely vegetable feeders. The family is an important one.

73

4a Front legs widened, fitted for burrowing. (Mole Crickets, Pygmy Crickets) Fig. 110.   Family 8, GRYLLIDAE

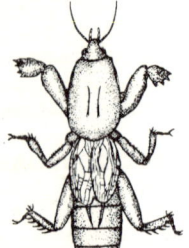

Fig. 110. *Gryllotálpa hexadáctyla* Perty. The Northern Mole Cricket.

Reddish brown, thickly covered with short fine hairs; claws, and veins of wings darker. Wings quite variable in length. Length of body 20-30 mm.

The mole crickets, though not often seen, never fail to attract attention when found. They burrow in mud at the sides of ponds and streams and are nocturnal in habits. Some persistent searching in favorable places should result in securing some specimens of this highly interesting insect for one's collection. They cause injury by feeding on the roots of plants.

The Pigmy Mole Crickets are similar in shape and habitat but much smaller (10 mm. or less) and belong here, though some would give them a separate family.

Figure 110

4b Front legs normal, not used for burrowing; organ of hearing if possessed, on first abdominal segment. Ovipositor short. 5

5a Pronotum long, (A) often reaching to or beyond tip of abdomen; tarsi of first and second legs with apparently two segments. (Grouse Locusts, Pygmy Locusts) Fig. 111.   Family 5, TETTIGIDAE

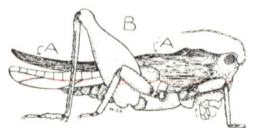

Fig. 111. *Acrydium arenosum* (Burm.) Sanded Grouse Locust. B, Side view; C, Top view. Grayish to blackish, sometimes with large white spot on back. Length 8-14 mm.

This family of Grouse or Pygmy Locusts has some 700 widely scattered species. All are small and, because of their long pointed pronotum (A) have a peculiar appearance. Since they hibernate as adults they often are represented in Spring insect collections.

Figure 111

74

5b Pronotum normal; front tarsi three segmented. (Locusts or Grass-hoppers) Fig. 112.
Family 4, LOCUSTIDAE

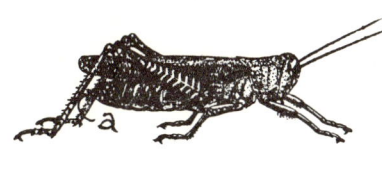

Figure 112

Fig. 112. *Melánoplus differentiàlis* (Thos.) Differential Grasshopper.

Varies in color from yellow through greenish yellow to blackish. Prominent diagonal stripes on femora and other markings black. Length 30-45 mm.

To this family belong the species of grasshoppers that have been responsible for heavy crop losses throughout the history of man. The Rocky Mountain Locust was particularly destructive in the early days in the West because of its migratory habits. Most species live and die in the field where they hatched. Some species pass the winter as adults, but in most cases the eggs are deposited in the ground in the late summer and hatch the following Spring.

6a Body flattened and oval; head covered with pronotum; swift on foot. (Cockroaches) Fig. 113.
Family 1, BLÁTTIDAE

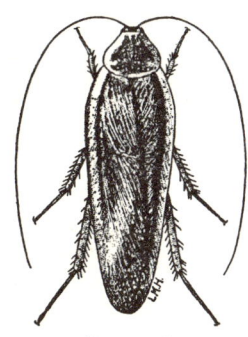

Figure 113

Fig. 113. *Parcoblátta pennsylvánica* De Geer The Pennsylvania Wood Roach. (after Lugger)

Pronotum dark brown, marked with yellowish; upper wings brown, with yellowish side margin. Wings of male as shown; of female only about half as long as abdomen. This seems to be our most abundant native roach. Length of body 13-25 mm.

Roaches are alike in being soft, smooth and slippery. Several species are fairly common and may be pests about the kitchen or in restaurants and store houses. They have long associated with man but greatly outdate him in antiquity. A beautiful pale green roach (*Panchlòra cubénsis* Sauss.) is sometimes found in bananas but does not establish itself in our climate.

6b Head free; body elongate; prothorax long and slim. 7

7a Front legs fitted for catching insect prey and held in a character- istic prayerful attitude. (The Praying Mantes) Fig. 114.

Family 2, MANTIDAE

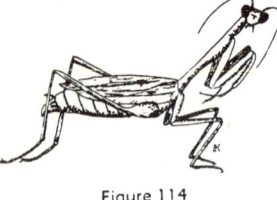

Figure 114

Fig. 114. *Stagomántis carolìna* (Johannson) The Carolina Mantis.

Females dark brown, sometimes greenish yellow; males gray or grayish brown. Length 45-55 mm.

These very alert hypocrites which appear pious but are ever awaiting the coming of some unfortunate insect, have been given many names down through the years from "prophets" to "mule killers" and "devil's horses". Something less than 2000 species are known, most of which are tropical. The Chinese Mantid which has been introduced into some parts of our country may measure 100 mm. or more.

7b Front legs normal; narrow, cylindrical, wingless insects. (The Walk- ingsticks) Fig. 115.

Family 3, PHÁSMIDAE

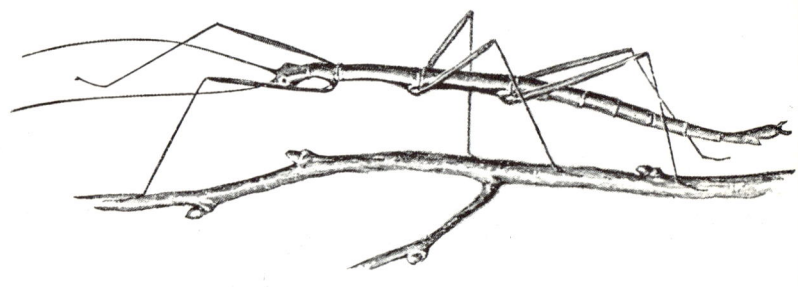

Figure 115

Figure 115. *Diapremomèra femoràta* (Say) The Walkingstick.

Colored in various shades of green, brown, gray and rarely pink. Length of body 65-100 mm.

These interesting insects are sometimes known as devil's darning needles and reputed to have fatal stings. They are wholly harmless and so ambitionless that they move very slowly. They are vegetable feeders. When motionless with legs and antennae extended in line with the body they strongly resemble a twig or stick and doubtless often thus elude their enemies.

ORDER DERMÁPTERA

1a **Second segment of tarsi normal, cylindrical, neither flattened or lobed.** **2**

1b **Second tarsal segment lobed or rather widely dilated. Fig. 116.**
Family 1, FORFICULIDAE

Fig. 116. *Forfícula auriculària* (L.) European Earwig.

Black or brownish, shining 12-15 mm. A frequent garden and household pest; widely distributed.

This is a large family. Its members are usually winged though some species are flightless.

Figure 116

2a **Antennae with but 11 to 15 segments, the fourth, fifth and sixth measured together, longer than the first. Fig. 117.**
Family 3, LABIIDAE

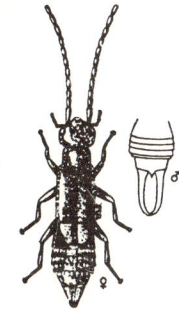

Fig. 117. *Lábia mìnor* (L.) The Small Earwig.

This little black species is cosmopolitan; 4-6 mm.

This family is a large one of many widely scattered species. They are usually flattened.

This is likely the most common earwig in many parts of our country. It often flies at lights. The collector will need to look closely to distinguish it from the small Staphylinids which it rather closely resembles in both form and habits.

Figure 117

2b **Antennae with 16 to 30 segments, the fourth, fifth and sixth measured together, seldom longer than the first. Fig. 118.**
Family 4, LABIDURIDAE

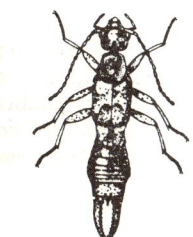

Fig. 118. *Euboréllia annúlipes* (Lucas) The Ring-legged Earwig (Kan. S.B.A.)

Blackish; legs light with dark rings or spots; elytra present but wings absent.

An Australian species the largest of all known Earwigs (40 mm.) belongs to this family.

Figure 118

ORDER COLEÓPTERA

1a Mouth parts reduced, front of head usually prolonged into a slender snout (beak). Gular sutures on under side of head fused into one or lacking. Tarsi 5 segmented, the 4th often very small. Prosternal sutures lacking. (Snout Beetles, Weevils, Engravers Beetles, etc.) Fig. 119.   Suborder RHYNCHÓPHORA....55

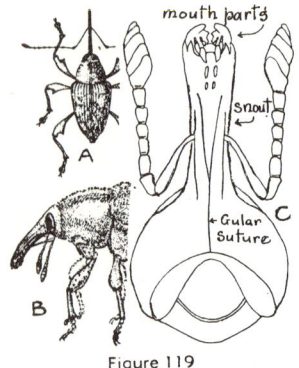

Figure 119

Fig. 119. A, dorsal view of a Snout Beetle; B, side view; C, ventral view of head and snout showing gular sutures, mouth parts and antennae.

This is a very large group of highly important beetles. They vary widely in size and shape: this is also true of the length of the snout. The larvae which are usually known as weevils feed, for the most part, within the stems, fruit and other parts of plants and are often very destructive.

1b Head not prolonged into a narrow cylindrical snout (beak). The two gular sutures distinct at both ends and not united. Prosternal sutures distinct. Fig. 120.   Suborder ÇOLEÓPTERA GENUINA.. .2

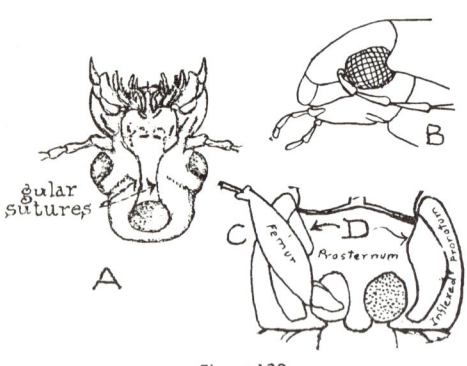

Figure 120

Fig. 120. A, Ventral view of head showing the two gular sutures, mouthparts, etc.; B, side view of head; C, ventral view of prothorax showing prosternal sutures. (D.)

A very large percentage of the beetles fall in this great group. They vary widely in size, shape, color, etc. Some are useful to man, others work against him.

2a Hind tarsi with the same number of segments as the fore tarsi...3

2b Hind tarsi with only four segments. Fore tarsi with five segments. (Heterómera) 36

3a All tarsi with five segments. (If the fourth segment is obscure as in Fig. 122a, take 4a.) Fig. 121. 5

Figure 121

3b All tarsi with less than five segments. 4

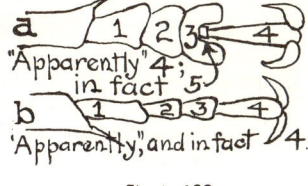

Figure 122

4a All tarsi with apparently four segments. (In many cases a very small obscure segment makes actually five.) Fig. 122. 47

4b All tarsi with apparently three segments. Fig. 123. 53

Figure 123

5a Outer lobe of galea of maxilla (B) palpiform; first ventral segment of abdomen completely divided by hind coxal cavities (C). Antennae* almost always filiform. (A) (Adephaga) Fig. 124. 6

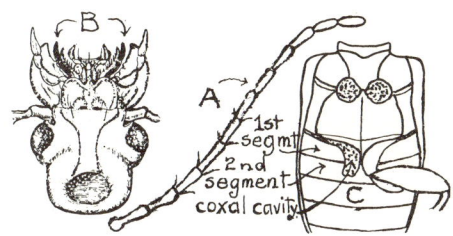

Figure 124

5b Outer lobe of galea of maxilla not palpiform; first abdominal segment not completely divided by hind coxal cavities. Antennae* of various shapes, usually not filiform. (See Fig. 41). Fig. 125. 11

Figure 125

6a Eyes divided, one pair on the upper surface and another pair on the lower surface of the head; Antennae very short and irregular (auriculate) (See Fig. 126). Legs for swimming. (Whirligig Beetles) Fig. 126. **Family 7, GYRÍNIDAE**

Fig. 126. *Dineùtes americànus* Say

Black with metallic luster; legs brownish yellow. Often seen in large numbers on surface of quiet water. Known as "apple-bug" or "penny-bug" on account of scent. Length 10-12 mm.

Whirligig beetles are well known, although the family is not large. The collector will find it good sport to attempt catching them. They seldom dive but are good at dodging. The family is a comparatively small one.

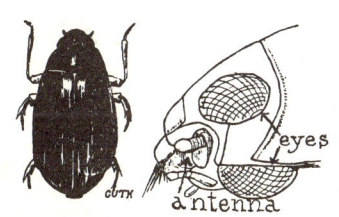

Figure 126

6b Eyes not divided; antennae filiform (thread-like) or nearly so. ...7

* If antennae are filiform the first ventral segment should always be examined.

7a Aquatic beetles; hind legs with fringes of long hair (and a long spur). (The Predacious Diving Beetles) Fig. 127.

Family 6, DYTÍSCIDAE

Figure 127

Fig. 127. *Ágabus disintegràtus* (Cr.)

Head and thorax dull reddish; elytra dull yellow; markings black. Length 7-8 mm.

Some members of this family are large beetles, averaging over an inch in length. The larvae, which live in water also, are known as water tigers and are highly destructive to fish fry and other small animals with which they are associated. These beetles fly readily and are often taken at lights.

There are more than 2000 known species.

7b Hind legs without fringes of long hair. 8

8a Small oval water beetles; antennae with 10 segments, entirely smooth; hind coxae forming large plates covering the base of the abdomen. (Crawling Water Beetles) Fig. 128.

Family 5, HALÍPLIDAE

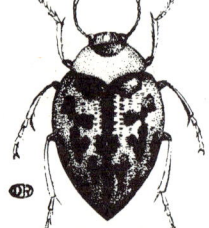

Figure 128

Fig. 128. *Halíplus triópsis* Say

Light brown yellow; spots on elytra black. In quiet waters. Length about 3.5 mm.

Our members of this family are all quite small. Although living in water, they are feeble swimmers. They are frequently found well below the surface. A fine water net and some good patience is necessary to get many of them.

8b Terrestrial beetles; antennae with 11 segments, with at least the apical 6 pubescent; hind coxa normal. 9

9a Head including the eyes almost always wider than the thorax; inner lobe of maxilla with movable hook at its end (A); clypeus extending laterally beyond the base of the antennae. (Tiger Beetles) Fig. 129.

Family 1, CICÍNDELIDAE

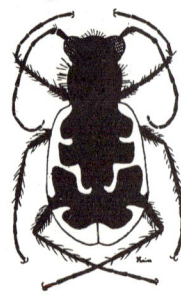

Figure 129

Fig. 129. *Cicindèla repánda* Dej.

Brownish-bronze with white markings. Underparts and legs greenish. Common on sandy banks of streams. Length 12-13 mm.

Some of the most beautiful beetles belong to this family. It is real sport to catch them. They are born hunters and know the tricks of the game. Often one must put them to flight to locate them, their protective coloration is so good. Then the beetle lights several feet in advance, but always facing the pursuer, ready to fly again as the latter approaches striking distance. Even when in the net they do not give up the fight but frequently escape. When fish fail to bite or game is scarce, try catching tiger beetles for a real thrill.

9b Head almost always narrower than the thorax;* inner lobe of maxilla without a movable hook at its end. (Fig. 43) Clypeus not extending beyond the base of the antennae. 10

10a Beetles of round convex form; not over 8 mm. in length. Scutellum concealed. Prosternum scoop-shaped, entirely covering the metasternum. Fig. 130.　　　　　　　Family 4, OMOPHRONIDAE

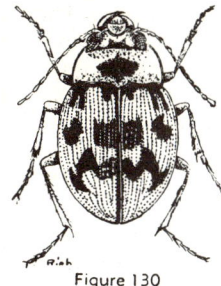

Figure 130

Fig. 130. Omophron tessellatum Say

Pale brownish yellow; with metallic green markings. Found under debris and buried in sand at edge of water courses. Length 6-7 mm.

These were formerly included with the ground beetles. It is a small family and has only the one genus.

10b Usually elongated in form. Very small to large in size; often black but sometimes brown, yellowish, or with brilliant metallic colors, etc.; highly variable. Fast running. (Ground Beetles) Fig. 131.
　　　　　　　Family 2, CARABIDAE

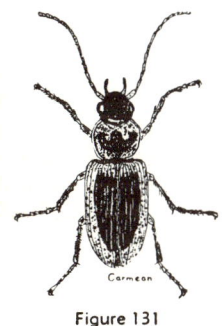

Figure 131

Fig. 131. Agonoderus comma (Fab.)

Yellowish brown with wide black stripe on each elytron. Antennae reddish brown, legs pale. One of our most common beetles: Often very abundant at lights. Length 5-6 mm.

Ground beetles are for the most part active only by night. During the day they hide under stones and debris. A great many species may be taken, especially in the spring, by looking under boards and stones lying on the ground. Black is the most usual color but many are beautifully marked. They range widely in size, and are beneficial in killing other insects.

11a Antennae lamellate, bearing flattened plates at end, as in Figs. 132 or 133. Legs often fitted for digging. 12

11b Antennae not lamellate. 15

* A few ground beetles have the head wider than the thorax and might seem to be tiger beetles. The genus **Elaphrus,** common on mud flats with about 20 North American species, is one of such. They differ from the tiger beetles by the antennae arising at side of head between base of mandible and the eye instead of on the front of head above the base of the mandible.

12a Plates composing antennal club flattened and capable of close apposition. Fig. 132. 13

Figure 132

12b Plates of antennal club not capable of close
apposition, usually but slightly flattened.
Fig. 133. 14

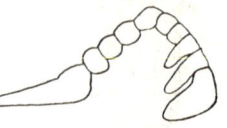

Figure 133

13a Abdomen with five visible ventral segments; epimera of the mesothorax not reaching the coxae (a). Elytra usually covered with tubercles. (The Skin Beetles) Fig. 134.   Family 98, TRÓGIDAE

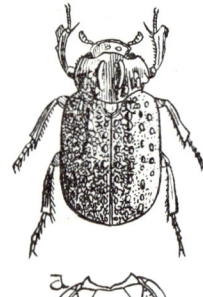

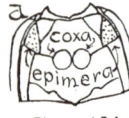

Figure 134

Fig. 134. *Tróx monachus* Hbst.

Dull grayish black, roughened with warty tubercles. One of a small family of heavy set thick
bodied beetles found on skins and bones of carrion. Length 13-16 mm.

One may often find several species of this little
family flying to the lights at night. An old slaugh-
ter house is a good place to look for them. They
are frequently so encrusted with dirt that they
must be cleaned before accurate identification is
possible.

13b Abdomen with six visible ventral segments, or if only five, then
the epimera of the metathorax reaching the coxae. (The Scarabae-
ids or Dung Beetles) Fig. 135.   Family 97, SCARABAEIDAE

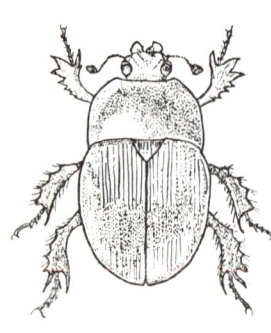

Figure 135

Fig. 135. *Geótrupes spléndidus* Fab.

Well rounded, metallic green, sometimes purple or bronze. Abundant in dung.
Length 13 to 17 mm.

Because of their style of antennae the
members of this family are called Lamel-
licorn Beetles. It is a large family ranging widely in size, color, shape, and habits. Our destructive white grubs which
grow up to be May Beetles belong here,
as do many other plant feeders. Some
species are scavengers and do no harm.

14a Antennae not elbowed. Mentum deeply notched, the ligula filling the notch. Fig. 136.   **Family 100, PASSALIDAE**

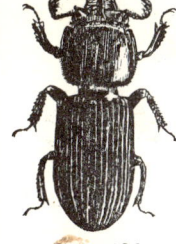
Figure 136

Fig. 136. *Pássalus cornùtus* Fab. The Horned Passalus.

Length 32-37 mm. Shiny black with a short horn bent forward on the top of the head. Both adults and larvae found in decaying wood. There is but this one species in our country. In the tropics several species occur and attain considerably greater size.

14b Antennae nearly always geniculate (elbowed); mentum entire. (The Stag Beetles). Fig. 137.   **Family 99, LUCANIDAE**

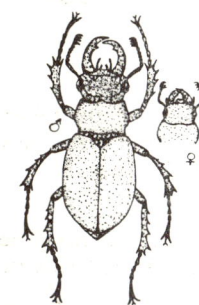
Figure 137

Fig. 137. *Pseudolucànus caprèolus* (L.) "The Pinching Bug."

Dark reddish brown, femora light brown. Mandibles of female only half as long as those of male, here shown. Frequently fly to lights. Length 22-35 mm.

We have only a few species of stag beetles but because of their threatening ways they are well known. The adults are said to live on plant secretions and honey dew. The larvae are found in decaying wood.

15a Hind legs modified for swimming; (Fig. 138) Antenna clavate or capitate, short, with 6 to 9 segments. (The genus *Sphaeridium* belonging here, does not have swimming legs.) (The Water Scavenger Beetles) Fig. 139.   **Family 8, HYDROPHILIDAE**

Figure 138

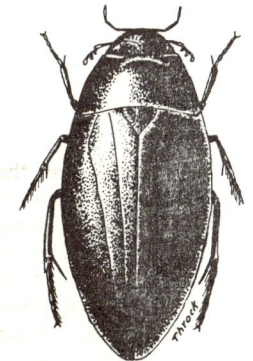
Figure 139

Fig. 139. *Hýdrous triangularis* (Say)

Black with olive tinge; shining, more so below. In water and flying to lights. Length 34-38 mm.

The members of this family are supposedly scavengers but there is good evidence that at least some species catch living insects or small fish. There are some small species that live in the dung of cattle and are shaped somewhat like Hister beetles but may be readily distinguished from them in not having truncate elytra.

15b Hind legs not modified for swimming. 16

16a Elytra covering less than half the length of the abdomen (Fig. 140A); wings folded under the short elytra when not in use; all the abdominal segments horny on top. 17

16b Elytra covering all or at least more than half of the abdomen; upper part of some of the abdominal segments membranous. . .18

17a Abdomen flexible and with 7 or 8 segments visible below. (Rove or Short-winged Scavenger Beetles) Fig. 140.

Family 16, STAPHYLÍNIDAE

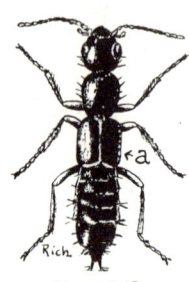

Figure 140

Fig. 140. *Paéderus littoràrius* Grav.

Head, elytra and tip of abdomen metallic bluish-black; thorax and first four dorsally exposed segments of abdomen yellowish red; legs brownish yellow. Length 4-6 mm.

This is a very large family, many species of which are very abundant in decaying organic matter. They have a peculiar way when disturbed of running around with the tip of the abdomen turned up as though threatening to sting. Of course, they have no sting but doubtless earn considerable protection from this ruse.

17b Abdomen rigid, with but 5 or 6 ventral segments. Usually brown, very small. Tarsi with but 3 segments. (Ant-loving Beetles) Fig. 141.

Family 17, PSELÁPHIDAE

Figure 141

Fig. 141. *Tmesíphorus cóstalis* Lec.

Black, shining; covered with short, appressed yellowish hairs. ♀ with shorter antennae 3.3 mm.

The family is a rather large one. They are often found under bark and stones and feed on the tiny animal life of their habitat. The "love" seems to be on the part of the ants for they give off a secretion which is apparently quite pleasing to the ants.

18a Small oval convex, very shiny beetles with conical tipped abdomen (a) exposed under broadly truncate elytra. Six or seven ventral abdominal segments. (The Shining Fungus Beetles) Fig. 142.

Family 21, SCAPHIDIIDAE

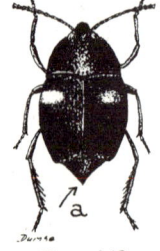

Figure 142

Fig. 142. *Scaphídium quadriguttátum* Say

Shining black with a reddish spot on each elytron. Found in fungi, on which it feeds. Length about 4 mm.

A variety *piceum*, wholly black, is about equally common. The family is a small one and relatively of small importance.

18b Not as in 18a. **19**
19a Abdomen with seven or eight visible ventral segments. **20**
19b Abdomen with less than seven ventral segments. **22**
20a Middle coxae separated from each other. Epipleurae absent. No
light-giving organs. (Net-Winged Beetles) Fig. 143.

Family 24, LÝCIDAE

Figure 143

Fig. 143. *Calópteron reticulàtum* (Fab.)

Dull orange yellow with black markings.
Length 12-20 mm. Unlike the fireflies, which
they strongly resemble, the members of this
family are diurinal.
They spend their day
hunting insects on
which they feed.

Figure 144

20b Middle coxae touching. Epipleura distinct. **21**

21a Head more or less completely covered by prothorax; episternum
of metathorax not sinuate (double curved) on inner side. (Fig. 144)
(Firefly Beetles) Fig. 145. Family 25, LAMPÝRIDAE

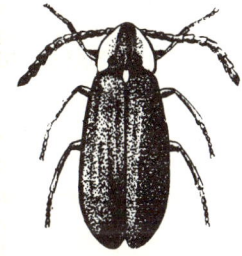

Figure 145

Fig. 145. *Lucidòta àtra* (Fab.)

Dull black; sides of thorax dull yellow with
reddish margin next to black mid-line. Length
8-11 mm.

The Fireflies live a sluggish life by day
but at dusk come out with a splendor unap-
proached by other insects. The fire flashes
apparently serve to attract the mate. In some
species the females are wingless and are
known as glow worms.

21b Head, if at all, less than half covered by the prothorax; episternum
of metathorax sinuate (with S curve) on inner side. (Fig. 144).
(Soldier Beetles, etc.) Fig. 146. Family 27, CANTHÁRIDAE

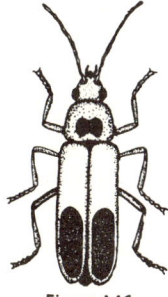

Figure 146

Fig. 146. *Chauliógnathus pennsylvánicus* De G.
The Soldier Beetle.

Thorax and elytra yellow marked with black;
head and underparts black. Very abundant in
late summer and fall on goldenrod. Length
9-12 mm.

The members of this family, in shape and
soft bodies, resemble the fireflies. They are diurnal and probably live on pollen and nectar of
flowers.

22a Abdomen with six ventral segments. 23

22b Abdomen with five ventral segments. 26

23a Very small oval, (from less than 1mm. to not over 3 mm.), convex, shining, brown or blackish beetles; usually covered with erect hairs. Eyes coarsely granulate. (Ant-like Stone Beetles). Fig. 147.   Family 14, SCYDMAENIDAE

Fig. 147. *Eumicrus motschulskii* Lec.

Dark reddish brown, rather thickly clothed with yellowish hairs. Length 1.7 mm. (after Blatchley.)

The members of this family are all small. They are found in damp places and often in the nests of ants. About 1000 species are known.

Figure 147

23b Not as in 23a. 24

24a Mostly large beetles, usually over 12 mm. long, either broadly flattened or heavy and in this latter case with elytra short, exposing two or three segments of abdomen. (The Carrion Beetles) Fig. 148.   Family 12, SILPHIDAE

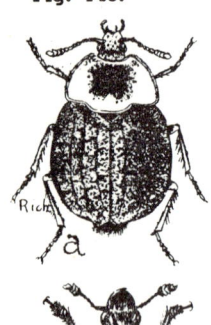

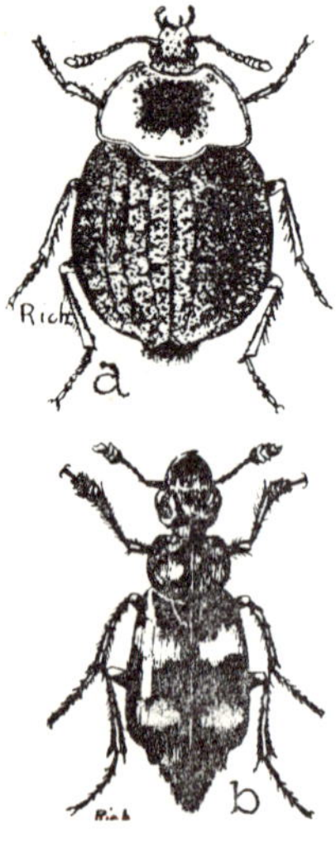

Fig. 148a. *Silpha americana* L.; 148b. *Necrophorus orbicollis* Say.

Much flattened. Thorax yellow with center spot black; elytra brownish with elevations darker. Fairly common on carrion. A beautiful beetle if it were not for its disgusting ways. Length 16-20 mm.

Several other species of this genus occur, all of them flattened and shaped somewhat like *americana*. Another genus *Necrophorus* is common. Its members are large, elongate and robust. They are black with brilliant vermilion markings on head, thorax, and elytra. They are known as burying beetles because of their habit of burying small carcasses as food for their larvae. The family also includes some minute species.

Figure 148

24b Seldom over 10 mm. in length. Cylindrical forms. 25

25a Hind coxae conical. Front coxae long with distinct trochantins. (The Soft-winged Flower Beetles) Fig. 149. Family 28, MELÝRIDAE

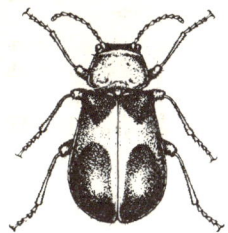

Figure 149

Fig. 149. *Cóllops quadrimaculátus* (Fab.)

Head, abdomen and femora black; thorax and elytra reddish-yellow; markings blue or bluish black. Readily taken by sweeping. Length 4-6 mm.

The members of this family prey on other insects. They are all small in size.

25b Hind coxae flat; covered with femora when at rest. Fourth tarsal joints equal to others. (The Checkered Beetles) Fig. 150.

Family 29, CLÉRIDAE

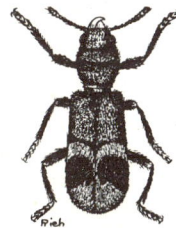

Figure 150

Fig. 150. *Enóclerus nìgripes* Say

Elongate-cylindrical, thickly clothed with hairs. Head, thorax and base of elytra dull red. Two cross bars on elytra black. Tips of elytra and space between black bars whitish. Length 5-7 mm.

Many of the adults of this family are predacious on bark feeding insects but a few species are destructive to cereal and animal products.

26a Antennae both elbowed and club-shaped. Hard, usually small, black or red and black beetles; elytra square-cut (truncate) (A) at end exposing two segments of abdomen. (Hister Beetles) Fig. 151.

Family 23, HISTÉRIDAE

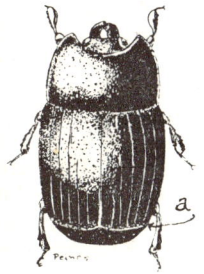

Figure 151

Fig. 151. *Platysòma depressum* Lec.

Shiny black, much flattened. Common under bark of logs. Length 3-4 mm.

Other members of this family live under bark and are greatly depressed. Many others live in carrion. They are usually much thickened. A few species have red markings on the elytra. The family has several thousand species.

26b Not as in 26a. **27**

27a Femora attached to end of trochanter or very near the end. Fig. 152. 28
Fig. 152. c, Coxa; t, trochanter; f, femur.

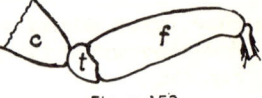
Figure 152

27b Femora attached to side of trochanter. Fig. 153. 29
Fig. 153. c, Coxa; t, trochanter; f, femur.

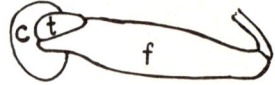
Figure 153

28a Antennae inserted on the front. Small beetles. (The Deathwatch and Drug-store Beetles.) Fig. 154. **Family 91, PTINIDAE**

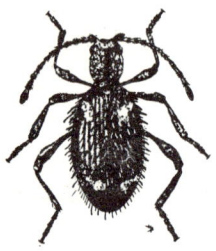
Figure 154

Fig. 154. *Ptinus fur* L.

Reddish brown, with 4 white spots on elytra. Found in places where meal and other foods are stored. Length about 3 mm.

Judged from human likes and dislikes, some insects have queer tastes. Some members of this and of the family *Anobiidae* live in drugs and other stored products seemingly poorly suited for food.

28b Antennae inserted before the eyes; (a); tibiae with spurs (b); first ventral not elongated. (Powder-Post Beetles.) Fig. 155.
Family 93, BOSTRICHIDAE

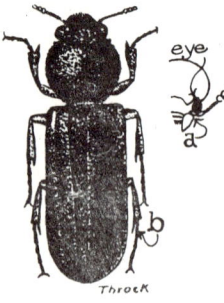
Figure 155

Fig. 155. *Ampricerus hamatus* (Fab.)

Dark brown, with scattered recumbent hairs. Elytra coarsely punctured. Length 7-9 mm.

The beetles of this family are dull colored and cylindrical in form. They feed in dry wood and often cause serious damage to lumber and to buildings. Their work is sometimes mistaken for that of termites.

29a Front coxae conical, projecting prominently from coxal cavity..:30

29b Front coxae globular or transverse, usually projecting but little from coxal cavity. 31

30a Hind coxae dilated into plates partly covering base of femora. Antennae with large three segmented club at end. (Skin Beetles) Fig. 156.   Family 64, DERMÉSTIDAE

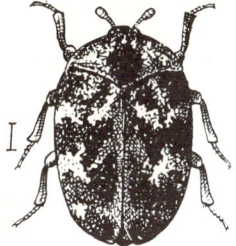

Figure 156

Fig. 156. *Anthrènus scrophulàriae* (L.) The Carpet Beetle.

Ovate, convex. Black, thickly covered with colored scales in black and white zig-zag transverse rows, interrupted by a bright red sutural stripe, through middle of back. This insect has been introduced from Europe and the adults may be frequently found in great abundance on the flowers of Spiraea in early summer. Length 2.5-3.5 mm. (From U.S.D.A.)

The Skin beetles do not constitute a large family but are very destructive to stored foods, furs, clothing, etc. They are the most persistent pests of the insect collection and every unguarded collection is sure to contain some living representatives of this family even though no pinned ones are present.

30b Hind coxae flat, not dilated into plates, fourth joint of tarsi equal to others. (Checkered Beetles) Fig. 157.   Family 29, CLERIDAE

Figure 157

Fig. 157. *Hydnócera pallípennis* (Say)

Black; antennae and legs pale; elytra dull yellowish with variable brownish or black markings. Length 3-5 mm. The checkered beetles may well be favorites with collectors. Although rather small in size their graceful form and varied color patterns, not infrequently brilliant, place them among the most beautiful beetles.

31a Front coxae transverse; hind coxae flat. .32
31b Front coxae globular. 33
32a Tarsi slender, first segment short; elytra never truncate. (Grain and Bark-gnawing Beetles.) Fig. 158.

Family 68, OSTOMÁTIDAE

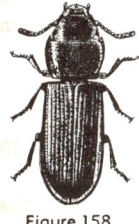

Figure 158

Fig. 158. *Tenebròides mauritánicus* (L.)

The Cadelle. Flattened; shiny black. A serious pest in mills, granaries and storehouses. Length 9-10 mm. (From U.S.D.A.)

This is a small family. Its members are black or reddish black. Most of them live under bark and are flattened so that they accomodate themselves to such cramped quarters.

32b Tarsi more or less dilated; first segment not short; elytra often truncate. (Sap-feeding Beetles.) Fig. 159.

Family 69, NITIDÚLIDAE

Fig. 159. *Omosita còlon* (L.)

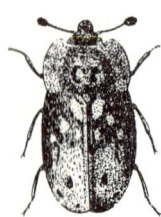

Figure 159

Brownish black with margins of thorax, four spots on base of elytra and a region of the apical ends dull yellow. On carrion and fungi. Length 2-3 mm.

The Sap-feeding beetles are a fairly sizable family. Many of them are flattened. Their feeding habits very greatly. They are usually quite small but a few species reach a length of 7 or 8 mm.

The sap oozing out on top of freshly cut tree stumps often attracts many species. If the collector will leave chips or small boards on the stumps the beetles will be hiding there when he comes again.

33a Prosternum with a spine which fits into a groove in the mesosternum. Fig. 160. 34

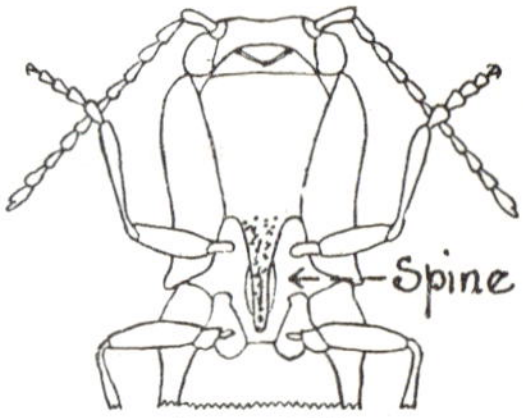

Spine

Figure 160

33b Not as in 33a. 35

34a The first and second abdominal segments fused; prothorax closely joined to mesothorax. (Metallic Woodborers) Fig. 161.

Family 54, BUPRÉSTIDAE

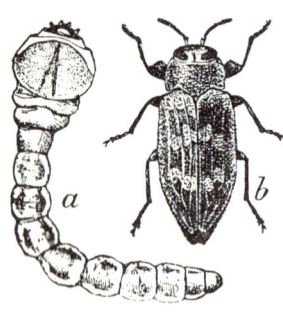

Figure 161

Fig. 161. *Chrysóbothris femorata* (Oliv.) (a, larva; b, adult.) The Flat Headed Apple Tree Borer.

Dark bronze with brassy metallic luster. Whitish markings on elytra variable. The larvae bore in the trunks of white oak, apple, and other trees. Length 8-16 mm. (From U.S.D.A.)

The Metallic Woodborers are favorites with collectors. Most of them look as though they were a product of our machine age. Some are very brilliantly colored. They run through a wide range of shapes and sizes.

90

34b Ventral segments not fused; Prothorax loosely joined to meso-thorax. (Click Beetles) Fig. 162.   Family 51, ELATERIDAE

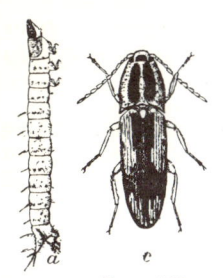

Figure 162

Fig. 162. *Monocrepidius vespertinus* Fab. (a and b, larvae; c, adult.)

Usually yellow beneath and dark reddish brown above, side markings on thorax and elytra yellow. Length 7-10 mm. (From U.S. D.A.)

The Click beetles are so named because of their unique scheme for righting themselves when turned on their backs. Two or three flips into the air is quite certain to land them right side up, then they lose no time in running away. The larvae are wire worms; many of them live in decaying logs but many others attack growing plants and accordingly are in ill repute with farmers and gardeners. The family is a large one.

35a Body flattened, middle coxal cavities open behind. (Flat Bark Beetles or Cucujids) Figs. 163, 170 and 174.

Family 72, CUCUJIDAE

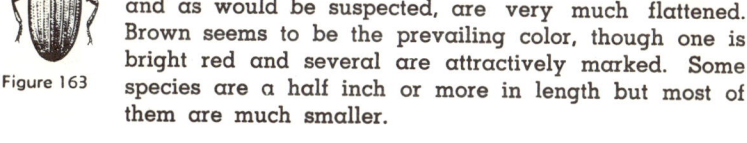

Figure 163

Fig. 163. *Oryzaephilus surinamensis* (L.)

Dark reddish brown. Readily distinguished by teeth on margin of thorax. A pest of stored grain and dried fruit. Length about 2.5 mm. (From U.S.D.A.)

Most of the members of this family live under bark and as would be suspected, are very much flattened. Brown seems to be the prevailing color, though one is bright red and several are attractively marked. Some species are a half inch or more in length but most of them are much smaller.

35b Front and middle coxal cavities closed behind. Body convex or cylindrical. (Pleasing Fungus Beetles) Figs. 164 and 181.

Family 73, EROTYLIDAE

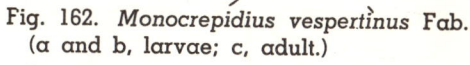

Figure 164

Fig. 164. *Languria trifasciata* (Say)

Cylindrical, tapering at both ends. Head and base and apex of elytra bluish black; thorax, middle of elytra and segments two to six, inclusive of antennae reddish yellow. Length 6-8 mm.

The Pleasing Fungus Beetles are for the most part smooth, shiny, elongate beetles that live in fungi. The larvae of *Languria mozardi* feed in the stems of clover. Many of the adults are marked with contrasting patterns of black and red.

36a Front coxal cavities closed behind. Abdomen with five ventral segments in part grown together. Fig. 165a. 37

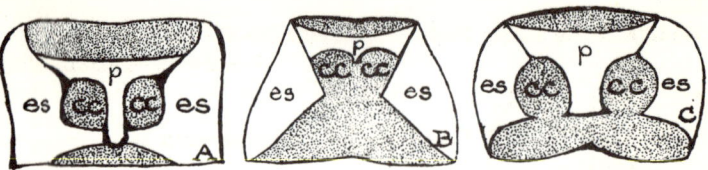

Fig. 165. A, Front coxal cavities closed behind and separated; B, widely open behind and confluent; C, open behind and separated; p, prosterum; es, episternum; cc, coxal cavities. (After Wickham.)

36b Front coxal cavities open behind. See Figs. 165B and C. 38

37a Next to last segment of tarsi spongy. (Lagriid Bark Beetles) Fig. 166.

Family 88, LAGRIIDAE

Fig. 166. *Arthromàcra aenèa glabricóllis* Blatch.

Elongate, convex. Brownish black with metallic iridescence. Length 10-13 mm.

This is a small family of beetles; found under bark and on leaves. They are rather uniformly dark colored but often have a metallic sheen.

Figure 166

37b Next to last segment of tarsi not spongy. (Darkling Beetles.) Fig. 167. Many Tenebrionids strongly resemble Fig. 166. They should be checked carefully for the tarsal characters.

Family 87, TENEBRIÓNIDAE

Fig. 167. A. *Tenèbrio mólitor* L.

Black, shining. 13-16 mm. Both adults and larvae very common where grain feeds are stored, especially if damp.

B. *Bolitothèrus cornùtus* (Panz.)

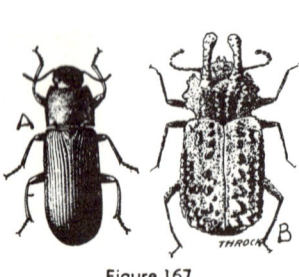

Dull brownish black. Thorax and elytra much roughened with large and small irregular tubercles. Males with two horns as pictured. When disturbed they "play possum" and strongly resemble bits of dry rotten wood or fungi among which they are found. Length 10-12 mm.

Figure 167

The Darkling beetles represent a large family. A large percentage are western forms. They vary in size from tiny little fellows to that of some of our largest beetles. A number of species are cosmopolitan pests of grain products. Many species are found under bark.

38a Head not strongly and suddenly constricted at base. **39**

38b Head strongly constricted at base, being suddenly narrowed behind. **41**

39a Middle coxae large; body long and narrow. Fig. 168.

Family 36, OEDEMÉRIDAE

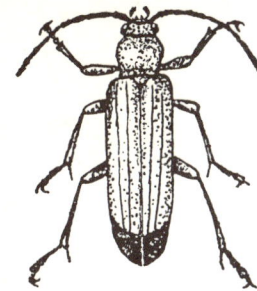

Figure 168

Fig. 168. *Načérda melanùra* L.

Dull yellow with purplish black spot at tip of elytra. Length 8-12 mm.

This family has some 800 species in its wide distribution. The adults are often taken at flowers. The species here pictured grows up in wet pine lumber and originally came from Europe.

39b Middle coxae not prominent. **40**

40a Mesosternum long; epimera of metathorax visible. (Melandryid Bark Beetles.) Figs. 169 and 178. Family 90, MELANDRYIDAE

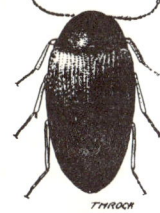

Figure 169

Fig. 169. *Eustróphinus bícolor* (Fab.)

Convex. Shiny black, sparsely pubescent. Abdomen, legs and four basal joints of antennae reddish yellow. Common under bark. Length 5-6 mm.

The members of this comparatively small family are found mostly in fungi and under bark. They are often thickly covered with silken hairs and range in size from 3 to 15 mm.

40b Mesosternum quadrate; epimera of metathorax covered. (Flat Bark Beetles) Figs. 170, 163 and 174.

Family 72, CUCUJIDAE

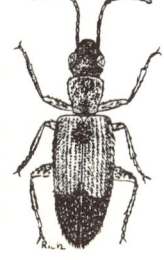

Figure 170

Fig. 170. *Teléphanus vèlox* Hald.

Slender, subdepressed, rather thickly clothed with hairs, pale brownish-yellow; head and apical ends of elytra darker. The antennae are frequently held in the characteristic position pictured. Length about 4 mm.

It will be noted that this rather important family falls at three places in the key. They are highly variable.

41a Side pieces of prothorax not separated from the pronotum by a suture. Base of prothorax narrower than elytra. **42**

41b Lateral suture of prothorax distinct; base of prothorax as wide as elytra. Antennae filiform. 46

42a Hind coxae large and prominent. 43

42b Hind coxae but slightly prominent, if at all. 44

43a Tarsal claws simple; head horizontal. (Fire-colored Beetles) Fig. 171.   Family 43, PYROCHROIDAE

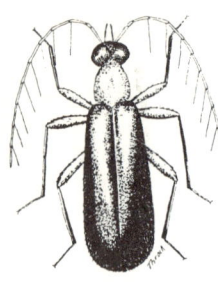

Figure 171

Fig. 171. *Dendròides bìcolor* Newn.

Reddish yellow. Head, antennae and elytra black. Specimen here shown, female. Branches of antennal joints longer in male. Length 9-13 mm.

This is a small family of beetles that in softness of body and shape somewhat resembles the fireflies. Red or yellow is usually a part of the color pattern and probably suggested the name. They are found under bark of partly decayed trees.

43b Front vertical. Claws toothed or cleft. (See Fig. 172). (Blister Beetles) Fig. 173.
                                    Family 39, MELOIDAE

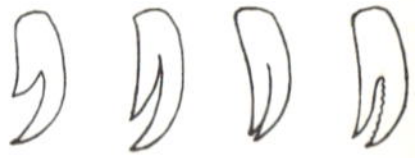

Figure 172

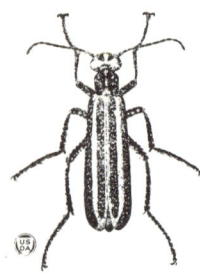

Figure 173

Fig. 173. *Epicaùta vittáta* Fab.

Sub-cylindrical. Dull clay yellow with black markings. Underparts black. A pest of potatoes and other garden plants. Length 12-18 mm. (From U.S.D.A.)

The Blister beetles are mostly medium sized insects, and contain cantharadine which raises blisters when applied to human skin. The larvae pass through several interesting stages in one of which they feed on grasshopper eggs, and so like many other insects are neither wholly good nor wholly bad.

44a Anterior coxae globular, not prominent. (Flat Bark Beetles) Figs. 174, 163 and 170.
                                    Family 72, CUCUJIDAE

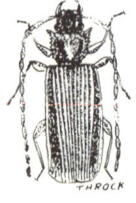

Figure 174

Fig. 174. *Bróntes dùbius* Fab.

Very thin. Dusky brown. Legs and margins of elytra paler. Antennae very long. Common under bark. Length 4-6 mm.

Both the adults and the larvae of this family are almost always flattened.

44b Anterior coxae conical, prominent. **45**

45a Eyes usually with a notch in their edge (emarginate), finely granulated; hind coxae touching or very close. Fig. 175.

Family 44, PEDILIDAE

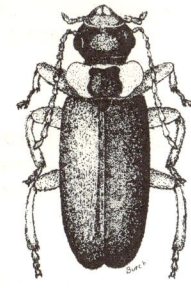

Figure 175

Fig. 175. *Pedilus labiàtus* (Say)

Black; thorax marked as pictured with yellowish red. Length 6-7.5 mm.

This family was formerly considered a tribe of the *Anthicidae*. They are elongate, cylindrical beetles; usually shining black; often with some yellow or red on thorax. They are frequently taken by sweeping.

45b Eyes entire (not notched), rather coarsely granulated; hind coxae usually separated. (Ant-like Flower Beetles) Fig. 176.

Family 45, ANTHICIDAE

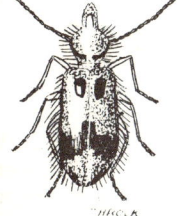

Figure 176

Fig. 176. *Notóxus monòdon* Fab.

Dull brownish yellow, thickly covered with grayish hairs. Thorax and elytra marked with black. This and some other members of the genus are peculiar in having a thick horn projecting forward from the front of the thorax. The head is usually held down and is not visible from above. Length 2.5 to 4 mm.

As the name indicates, many of the members of this interesting family are shaped like ants. They are beautifully marked and quite abundant.

46a Hind coxae plate-like, abdomen usually pointed (a). (Tumbling Flower Beetles) Fig. 177.   Family 37, MORDELLIDAE

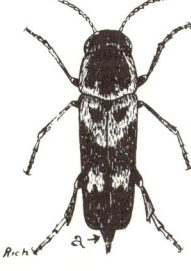

Figure 177

Fig. 177. *Mordélla oculàta* Say

Antennae, tibiae and tarsi dull red; head, thorax and abdomen blackish with yellow and gray markings. Length 5-7 mm.

The Tumbling Flower Beetles are so named because of their habit of tumbling actively about when disturbed until out of reach of the enemy. They are wedge shaped with arched body and head bent down. Most of the rather large number or species are of small size.

46b Hind coxae not plate-like. (Melandryid Bark Beetles) Figs. 178 and 169.   **Family 90, MELANDRYIDAE**

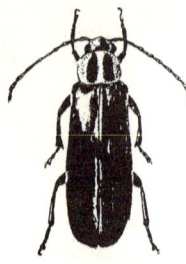

Fig. 178. *Ósphya vàrians* (Lec.)

Black, sparsely clothed with fine gray prostrate hairs; margin and middle of thorax reddish yellow. Length 5-8 mm.

Two of the larger and more common species are *Pénthe oblíquata* Fab. and *Pénthe pimèlia* Fab. Both are black, the latter wholly so, while the former has the scutellum covered with rust-red hairs.

Figure 178

47a Tarsi in reality with five segments, the fourth very small and hidden between prongs of third. (See Fig. 123) **50**

47b Only four tarsal segments. **48**

48a First four ventral abdominal segments fused. Tibiae dilated, armed with rows of spines for digging. (Variegated Mud-loving Beetles) Fig. 179.   **Family 58, HETEROCERIDAE**

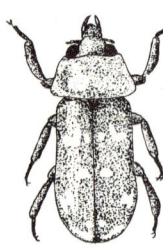

Fig. 179. *Heterócerus ventràlis* Melsh.

Black covered with brownish and yellowish hairs; the latter in three indistinct cross bands. Length 6-7 mm.

The members of this little family are found in burrows at the edge of our water courses. At night they are sometimes found in great numbers at lights. Many of the other species are smaller than *ventralis*.

Figure 179

48b Ventral segments of abdomen not grown together, front coxae globose. **49**

49a Tarsi slender. (Handsome Fungus Beetles.) Figs. 180 and 189.   **Family 83, ENDOMYCHIDAE**

Fig. 180. *Aphorísta vittáta* (Fab.)

Shiny, brownish red. Markings on thorax and elytra black. Length 5-6 mm.

Look in decaying wood, bracket fungi and under bark for the Pleasing Fungus Beetles. There are about 1000 species known. Some large and brilliantly colored are found in the tropics.

Figure 180

49b Tarsi more or less dilated and spongy beneath. (Pleasing Fungus Beetles.) Figs. 181 and 164. Family 73, EROTYLIDAE

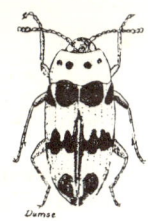

Figure 181

Fig. 181. *Ischyrus quadripunctàtus* (Oliv.)

Convex. Thorax and elytra yellowish red. Head and markings on thorax and elytra black. Length 7-8 mm.

This beautiful beetle is found hibernating in large numbers under bark and logs. That is also true of *Megalodácne fasciàta* Fab. which is considerably larger (10-15 mm.) and displays less red.

This family numbers more than 2000 species.

50a Body elongate; antennae almost always long, often as long as the body or longer. Base of antennae usually partly surrounded by eyes. (Long Horned Wood-boring Beetles.) Fig. 182.
Family 101, CERAMBÝCIDAE

50b Body usually short, more or less oval; antennae short, not at all surrounded by eyes. 51

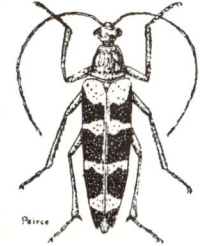

Figure 182

Fig. 182. *Typócerus velùtina* (Oliv.)

Head, thorax and antennae black. Elytra reddish brown with yellow cross bars. Common on flowers such as New Jersey Tea, Purple Headed Cone Flower, etc. Length 10-14 mm.

The Long Horned Woodborers are strong favorites with collectors. Theirs is a large family varying widely in shape, size, and color. Many species are destructive to trees and shrubs, while the larvae of some species live in the stems of herbaceous plants. Some 20,000 species are known.

51a Small (less than 3 mm.) shining, very compact, rounded, convex beetles; elytra wholly covering abdomen; last three segments of antennae enlarged forming a club. (Shining Flower Beetles.) Fig. 183.
Family 84, PHALÁCRIDAE

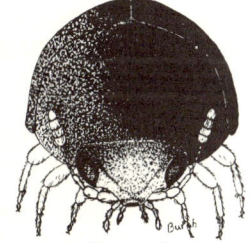

Figure 183

Fig. 183. *Phalácrus símplex* Lec.

Red-brown or blackish; legs and antennae pale. Length 2-2.3 mm.

This family which has some 500 species in our region is abundantly represented on our summer and fall flowers and later in debris where they hibernate.

51b Not as in 51a. 52

52a Front prolonged into a broad quadrate beak. Elytra exposing tip of abdomen (a). (Seed Weevils) Fig. 184.

Family 103, BRÚCHIDAE

Figure 184

Fig. 184. *Acanthoscélides obtéctus* (Say)

The Common Bean Weevil. Black, clothed with grayish pubescence. Elytra marked with obscure bands. Altogether too common in stored beans. Length about 3 mm. (From U.S.D.A.)

This family is small but very important. The larvae are universal pests of the larger seeds of Leguminous plants. The eggs are laid in most cases when the pods are quite small and develop within the growing seed. It is a rather reckless thing to do, for many of the tiny grubs lose their lives on the dinner table. Some species run a series of generations in stored seeds. If one will collect the seeds of different legumes and bottle them, the beetles, as well as their parasites which are also likely to be represented, may easily be collected when they emerge.

52b Front not prolonged into a beak. Abdomen usually wholly covered with elytra. Larvae and adults live on leaves of plants, (Leaf Beetles) Fig. 185.   Family 102, CHRYSOMÉLIDAE

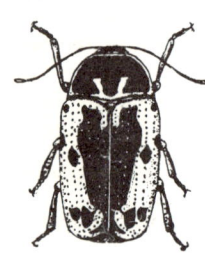

Figure 185

Fig. 185. *Chryptocéphalus mutàbilis* Melsh.

Heavy, subcylindrical. Shiny, reddish brown with markings on thorax and elytra yellow. The males have spots on thorax and elytra black or very dark. Length 4-6 mm.

This is a very large and important family. Few plants escape the ravages of some species of leaf beetle. They closely rival the Longhorns in interest and beauty for collections though they average smaller in size. Their greater abundance makes up for this seeming handicap.

53a Elytra short, covering only about half of body; antennae usually clubbed, occasionally bead-like; tarsi sometimes with but two segments; less than 4 mm. in length. (Ant-loving Beetles) Fig. 186.

Family 17, PSELÁPHIDAE

Figure 186

Fig. 186. *Rhexídius canaliculàtus* Lec.

Pale brownish-yellow with thick pubescence. Length 1.2 mm.

The members of this large family of tiny beetles are usually brown or yellowish. They live in much the same localities as the ants and are said to associate very familiarly with them.

53b Not as in 53a. **54**

54a Tarsal claws toothed or appendiculate. (Fig. 187). First ventral abdominal segment with distinct curved coxal lines. (Lady Beetles). Fig. 188.

Family 85, COCCINÉLLIDAE

Figure 187

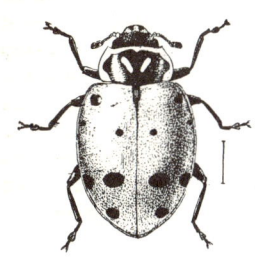

Figure 188

Fig. 188. *Hippodàmia convérgens* Guer.

The Convergent Lady Beetle.

Head and thorax black, marked with pale yellow. Elytra orange red with a common scutellar spot and six small spots on each, black. (Part of the spots are not always present) Underparts black. Length 5-6 mm. (From U.S.D.A.)

Lady beetles have long been favorites with man. They protect his plants from destruc-tiion and entertain his children. While many lady beetles are spotted, some are plain colored and others striped. Many spotted insects of this size are not lady beetles as the beginner sometimes supposes. They range in length from 1mm. to almost 10 mm.

54b Tarsaı claws simple. First ventral abdominal segment without coxal lines. (Handsome Fungus Beetles). Figs. 189 and 180.

Family 83, ENDOMÝCHIDAE

Figure 189

Fig. 189. *Endómychus biguttátus* Say

Elytra red marked with black. Head, antennae, legs, thorax, and scutellum black. Length about 4 mm.

It will be noted that this family appears at two places in the key. They are very interesting beetles though not economically important.

Many fungus-feeding beetles may be easily reared by confining fungi in tight containers until the larvae have had time to mature and emerge. Of course, fungi that is sufficiently aged to have collected eggs should be selected.

55a Beak absent or very short and broad. Antennae short and always elbowed. Tibia usually with teeth. (Engraver Beetles) Fig. 190.

Family 109, SCOLÝTIDAE

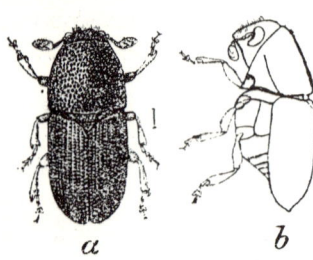

Figure 190

Fig. 190. *Scólytus rugulòsus* Ratz. (a, dorsal view; b, side view.) The Shot-hole Borer.

Blackish; antennae, tibiae, tarsi and apex of elytra reddish brown. Does serious damage to fruit trees. Length 2-2.5 mm. (From U.S.D.A.)

The Scolytids vary widely in form but are much alike in being exceedingly destructive. Because of their uniquely designed galleries in the cambium of tree trunks they are called "engraver beetles." The lumbering industry has paid a heavy toll to them. Many species are very small.

55b Tibia without teeth on outer edge. Beak usually longer than broad. 56

56a Antennae without a distinct club; not elbowed. Body long, slim, usually cylindrical. (Primitive Weevils) Fig. 191.

Family 104, BRÉNTIDAE

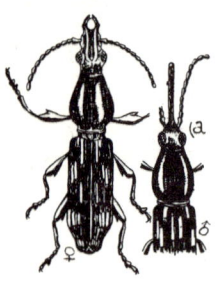

Figure 191

Fig. 191. *Eùpsalis minùta* Drury

Subcylindrical. Dark reddish brown with yellowish markings on elytra. The entire drawing is of the female. The males average larger than the females and have instead of the heavy mandibles a long, fairly straight snout projecting in line with the body to a length nearly equal to the thorax (a). Found under bark of dead or dying oaks, and other trees. Length 7-17 mm. (From Blatchley and Leng's Rhynchophora of N.E. America.)

Less than a thousand Primitive Weevils are known. Most of these are tropical woodborers. Only a few species are known for our region.

56b Antennae with distinct club; but either straight or elbowed.....57

57a Stout gray and black checkered beetle, 12-18 mm. long. Antennae not elbowed but with small oval club (a). But one species in our country. (New York Weevil) Fig. 192.   Family 105, BÉLIDAE

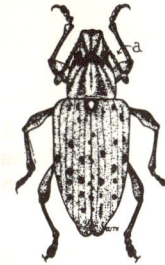

Fig. 192. *Ithýcerus noveboracénsis* (Forst.)

Black, clothed with gray and brown prostrate hairs arranged in interrupted stripes on thorax and elytra. Scutellum whitish. Breeds in bur oak and is destructive to fruit trees. It is the only representative of its family. Length 12-18 mm.

Figure 192

57b Not as in 57a. 58

58a Beak always short and broad. Palpi flexible. Thorax with transverse raised line. Antennae almost always not elbowed. (Fungus Weevils) Fig. 193.   Family 106, PLATYSTÓMIDAE

Fig. 193. *Eupàrius marmòreus* (Oliv.)

Robust dusky brown with irregular pattern of pale brown and gray scales on thorax and elytra. Bar of black on each elytron. Legs ringed with gray and black. Common under bark on dead stumps of willow, maple, etc. Length 4-9 mm.

This family has its largest representation in the tropics. Our species appear to be fungus feeders and are found in proximity to fungi on logs and stumps.

Figure 193

58b Snout often long and curved downward. Palpi rigid. Antennae almost always elbowed (a). (Typical Snout Beetles) Fig. 194.

Family 107, CURCULIÓNIDAE

Fig. 194. *Hypéra punctàta* Fab.

The Clover Leaf Weevil.

Convex, robust. Black, so clothed with gray, brown, and yellowish scales as to be much striped and mottled. Thorax with narrow midline and a wavy one on either side, light. (From U.S.D.A.)

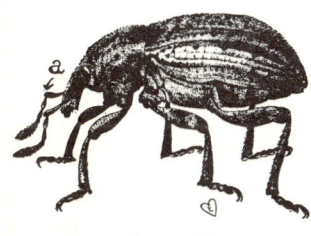

Figure 194

The Curculionids comprise a large and very important family. Some serious pests of corn and small grain belong here. Many of the "worms" in fruit and nuts are the larvae of snout beetles. Thus a long list of complaints might be registered against these interesting beetles, but they feel that they must live and have chosen to let man pay the bill.

ORDER THYSANOPTERA

1a Ovipositor of females saw-like. (Fig. 197B). Front wings largest; males with rounded abdomen, females conical. 2

1b Ovipositor unmodified. Many species wingless, the two pairs of wings similar when present; abdomen of both sexes conical. Fig. 195.   **Family 4, PHLOEOTHRIPIDAE**

Figure 195

Fig. 195. *Neoheegèria verbásci* (Osborn) The Mullein Thrips.

These tiny black thrips may be found at almost any season of the year and in almost any plant of the Common Mullein. They are usually most abundant among the woolly hairs of the younger leaves at the center of the plant.

Most of the members of this family are predaceous.

2a Ovipositor turning upward. Fig. 196.
                               Family 1, AEOLOTHRÍPIDAE

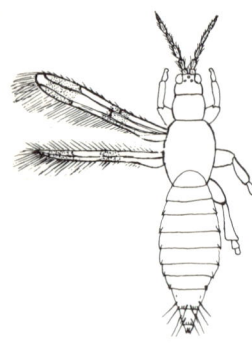

Figure 196

Fig. 196. *Aelóthrips fasciátus* (L.) The Banded Thrips.

Dark brown or yellowish with bands on wings. Length 1.6 mm. Predacious on other thrips, aphids and mites.

In this family the front wing is broad, giving the family the name of Broadwinged Thrips. Most of the species are predacious and should therefore be helpful.

2b Ovipositor turning downward (B). Fig. 197.
                               Family 2, THRÍPIDAE

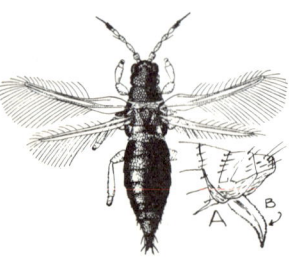

Figure 197

Fig. 197. *Heliothrips haemorrhoidàlis* (Bouche) The Greenhouse Thrips. A, tip of abdomen showing ovipositor B. Dark brown. Feeds on foliage of greenhouse plants. Larvae white. Length about 1 mm. (U.S.D.A.)

This largest family contains some of the most seriously destructive thrips. About 200 species are known with many more, of course, to be found.

ORDER CORRODENTIA*

1a Adults usually winged; 2-segmented tarsi; antennae with 13 segments. 2

1b Adults winged or wingless; 3-segmented tarsi; antennae with 13 or more segments. 3

2a Forewing with vein Cu_{1a} fused to vein M for a short distance forming a closed cell about in the middle of the wing. Fig. 198.

Family 1, PSOCIDAE

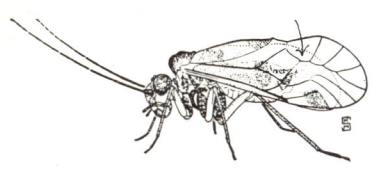

Figure 198

Fig. 198. *Psocus striatus* Walker.

Medium size (4.5 mm.) brown; forewings 3.5 mm. hyaline except for brown spot in stigma and another on posterior margin about midway (sometimes connecting with other across wing); eyes large and black; found on fence rails and at lights.

2b Forewing with vein Cu_{1a} not fused to media, but if connected then joined by a crossvein. Fig. 199.   Family 2, CAECILIIDAE

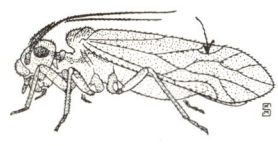

Figure 199

Fig. 199. *Caecilius manteri* Somm.

Small (2.5 mm.) buff color with golden brown eyes; fuscous lateral stripe; tan forewings about 2 mm. long, with brown veins in distal two-fifths; taken from dried corn.

3a Depressed individuals; usually wingless, if wings present then with veins and carried flat over abdomen; head prognathous (jaws extending forward). Fig. 200.   Family 9, LIPOSCELIDAE

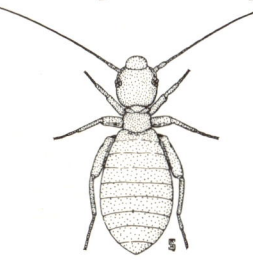

Figure 200

Fig. 200. *Lipóscelis* sp.

Small (1.2 mm.) light tan, depressed individuals with meso- and metanotum fused; often taken in libraries, houses, or animal nests.

* Dr. Kathryn M. Sommerman, who forgets more every day about the Corrodentia than many of us will ever know, kindly furnished the keys, descriptions and drawings for this order. She would be glad to correspond with any one who is collecting this group. She may be addressed % Natural History Survey, Urbana, Ill.

103

3b Plump individuals; well developed wings carried roof-like; veination as in Psocidae; head hypognathous (mouthparts extending downward). Fig. 201.   Family 3, MYOPSOCIDAE

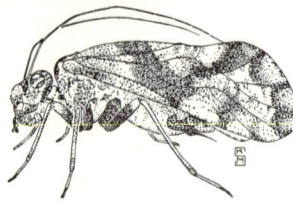

Fig. 201. *Lichenomìma* sp.

Rather large (6 mm.) mottled brown and white; forewings 5 mm.; 3-segmented tarsi; 13 segmented antennae; eyes light, with two dark stripes; usually found on tree trunks and rocks.

Figure 201

ORDER MALLÓPHAGA

1a Maxillary palpi with four segments; antennae clubbed, four segments. 2

1b Maxillary palpi wanting; antennae setiform, with 3 or 5 segments. 3

2a All tarsi with two claws; head broad, triangular. Host, poultry and wild birds. Fig. 202.   Family 1, MENOPÓNIDAE

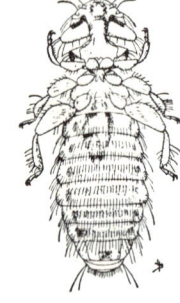

Fig. 202. *Eomenacánthus stramíneus* (Nitz.)

The Chicken Body Louse (U.S.D.A.)

It is found on turkeys, chickens, peacocks and pigeons, 2-2.5 mm.

This is a very important family. Many of the biting lice found on wild birds, belong to this family.

Figure 202

2b Only one claw or none on second and third legs. Host, guinea pigs. Fig. 203.   Family 5, GYRÓPIDAE

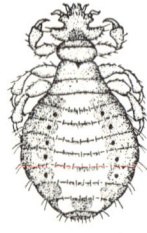

Fig. 203. *Gýropus ovàlis* Nitz.

Oval Guinea Pig Louse (After Osborn)

Most of the members of this relatively small family infest rodents and some other mammals of Central and South America. The above and another species have been scattered world wide by the guinea pig.

Figure 203

3a Antennae with five segments; tarsi two clawed; meso— and meta thorax fused. Host, birds. Fig. 204.   Family 6, PHILOTHERIDAE

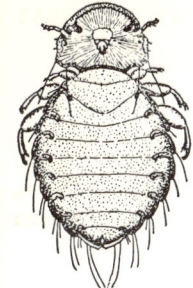

Fig. 204. *Goniocòtes hologáster* Nitz.

The Fluff Louse, Imm. (after Mote)

This is the largest family of biting lice. Not only our domestic birds but many of the wild ones harbor one or more species of these pests.

Chicken lice should not be confused with Mites which have eight legs and are not insects at all.

Figure 204

3b Antennae usually with three segments; tarsi with but one claw. Host, mammals. Fig. 205.   Family 8, TRICHODÉCTIDAE

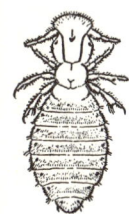

Fig. 205. *Trichodéctes òvis* L.

The Biting Sheep Louse (after Mote)

This is a very important family. Each of our domestic mammals has one or more species of the biting lice and while they feed only on the hair and skin scales, they may be very annoying. Many wild mammals have their own species also.

Figure 205

ORDER ANOPLÙRA

1a Compound eyes well developed; front of head short. 2
1b With only vestigial or no eyes; front of head much elongated.
Fig. 206.   Family 3, HAEMATOPÍNIDAE

Fig. 206. *Linógnathus vítuli* (L.)

The Long-nosed Cattle Louse

Host, cattle; widely scattered; 2.5 mm.
Members of this important family infest all of our domestic mammals while still other species are found on squirrels, rabbits, rats and many other wild mammals.

It is to be remembered that while the Mallophaga are found on both birds and mammals the members of the Anoplura are strictly confined to mammals. They are often serious pests and may cause heavy losses.

Figure 206

2a Body elongated, without lateral abdominal lobes. Host, man and other primates. Fig. 207.   Family 2, PEDICULIDAE

Fig. 207. *Pediculus humànus* (L.)

The Human Louse (U.S.D.A.)

The subspecies *corpòris* is the body louse, while the subspecies *humànus* is the head louse.

There are but three species in this full family; this one belonging very definitely to "us." The other two infest monkeys and apes.

Figure 207

2b Body crab-like, with lateral abdominal lobes. Host, man. Fig. 208.
                     Family 5, PHTHIRIDAE

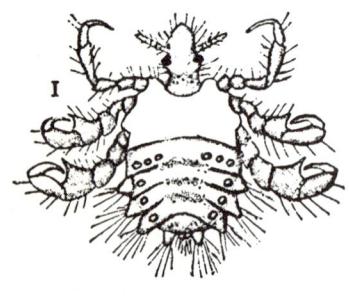

Fig. 208. *Phthírus pùbis* (L.)

The Crab Louse. (U.S.D.A.)

This disgusting parasite lives among the hairs of the armpits and genital regions of its host. It has been long known and is widely distributed. Its size, 2 mm. or less in length and width and rather pale color makes it difficult to see. The legs are reddish while the body is whitish with two darker spots. Ewing has described *P. gorillae* which infests the gorilla.

Figure 208

ORDER HEMÍPTERA

1a Antennae shorter than the head, frequently hidden in grooves beneath the eyes; mostly aquatic insects. 23

1b Antennae longer than the head; not hidden (except in Phymatidae). 2

2a Antennae with less than 5 segments. 5

2b Antennae with five segments. 3

3a Tibiae with several rows of heavy spines. Small, shining, black or dark beetle-like bugs with convex scutellum covering most of abdomen (A) (Negro Bugs); or flatter, dull colored (sometimes bright metalic) with triangular scutellum (B) (Burrower Bugs). Fig. 209.

Family 2. CYDNIDAE

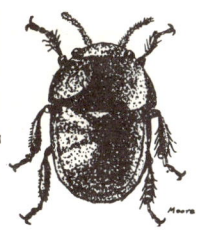 

Figure 209A   Figure 209B

Fig. 209A. *Galgupha atra* A. & S. Black, shining; very convex, 5-6 mm. 209B. *Pangeus bilineatus* Say Reddish black, 6-8 mm. (Kan. S.B.A.)

The family contains two subfamilies of bugs that are quite different in appearance. We are accordingly showing one of each.

3b Without strong spines on tibiae. 4

4a (a, b, c) Scutellum very large and convex, rounded behind and covering most of abdomen. (A) (Shield-backed Bugs). Fig. 210.

Family 1. SCUTELLÉRIDAE

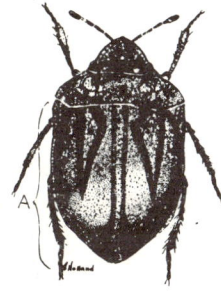

Figure 210

Fig. 210. *Homaemus bijugis* Uhler

Ground color yellowish tan ranging from light to darker in different specimens. Head black with lateral margins, reddish tan. Diverging stripes on thorax and scutellum formed by numerous black punctures. Length 6-8 mm.

In the tropics, members of this family are often highly colored. The rather abundant members of our comparatively few species have more somber tones.

4b Scutellum triangular, pointed behind; usually flattened shield shaped bugs. (Stink Bugs) Fig. 211.   Family 3. PENTATÓMIDAE

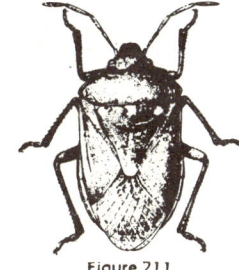

Figure 211

Fig. 211. *Chlorochroa sayi* Stal.

Say Stink Bug.

Bright green, spots as pictured at base of scutellum orange, tip of scutellum whitish; a western species 15-17 mm.

This family contains 5000 species of many colors and sizes. The shield shape usually prevails so that they can be told at a glance.

4c Head pointed in front, narrow and longer than broad; often with a distinct neck. Beak not reaching middle coxae. (A few Assassin Bugs having five segments in the antennae) (See 12a Fig. 219).

Family 12, **REDUVIIDAE**

5a Small insects. Front wings resembling lace. (Lace Bugs.) Fig. 212.

Family 9, **TINGITIDAE**

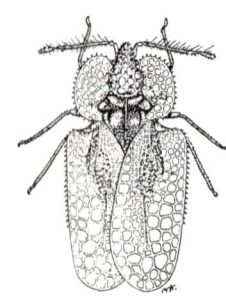

Figure 212

Fig. 212. *Corýthuca ciliàta* (Say)

The Sycamore Lace Bug.

Body black; antennae and legs yellowish. Upper surface milk white except a fuscous mid-midle spot. Common on leaves of sycamore, which it discolors and causes to fall prematurely. Length about 4 mm. (From U.S.D.A.)

The Lace Bugs surely live up to their name for they are daintily dressed with wings that look as though they had been made by some expert lace knitter. Many are oval in outline while some are elongate. Nymphs and adults are found together, feeding on the underside of leaves of many plants.

5b Not as in 5a. 6

6a Tarsal claws arising at sides near the base of last segment instead of at its apex. Fig. 213A. 7

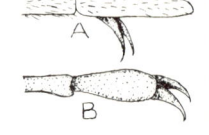

Figure 213

6b Tarsal claws arising from the end of tarsus in the normal way. Fig. 213B. 8

7a Legs long with hind femora reaching well past the tip of abdomen. (Water Striders) Fig. 214.

Family 24, **GÉRRIDAE**

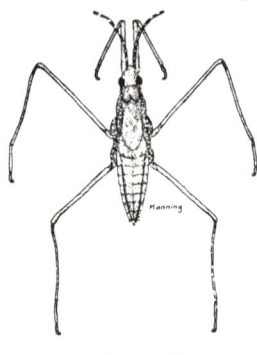

Figure 214

Fig. 214. *Gérris remígis* Say

Above brown to reddish brown; reddish brown on sides. First joint of antennae nearly as long as next three joints combined. No median carina or pronotum. Length 14-16 mm.

The legs of the Water Striders are long and slender, for they are used to skate about on the surface film of quiet water. They are frequently found in large groups. Many species have two forms, winged and wingless, with sometimes a third short-winged form. They live on other insects that fall into the water.

7b Small insects with shorter legs, the hind femora but slightly if at all reaching past the tip of abdomen. (Smaller Water Striders) Fig. 215.   **Family 25, VELIIDAE**

Figure 215

Fig. 215. *Microvèlia boreàlis* Bueno

Velvety brown and blackish with streaks of silver pubescence. Length 1.6-2 mm.

These little fellows walk on the surface film instead of boldly skating around as the Gerrids do. It is a small family.

8a Head equal to or longer than the thorax. (Water Measurers) Fig. 216.   **Family 23, HYDROMÉTRIDAE**

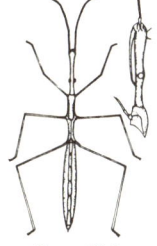

Figure 216

Fig. 216. *Hydrómetra martíni* Kirk.

Brown, often with tinges of blue; wings whitish with dark veins. Length 8-11 mm.

This is a small family of slender, slow-moving insects. They walk on the surface film in stagnant water pools. Just how they "measure the water" or of what value their work becomes is not readily apparent.

8b Head shorter than the thorax. 9

9a Beak with 4 segments. Fig. 217. 15

9b Beak with but 3 segments. 10

10a Front femora greatly thickened and much modified for catching insect prey (A) (Beak in fact with 4 segments but only 3 usually apparent) (Ambush Bugs) Fig. 218.   **Family 11, PHYMÁTIDAE**

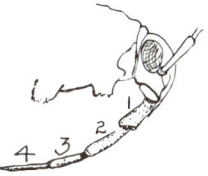

Figure 217

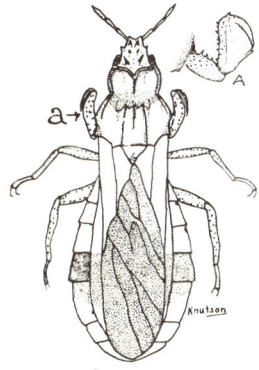

Figure 218

Fig. 218. *Phýmata eròsa fasciàta* (Gray)

Yellow or greenish yellow marked as shown, pale to reddish brown; legs not annulated. Length 9-12 mm.

The Ambush bugs lie in wait in the flowers of the *Compositae* and other plants for insect visitors. They are so shaped and colored as to blend into their surroundings and to be quite inconspicuous. The front legs, with large spine-covered femora, are adapted for catching and holding their insect prey. They are very common in the fall but not many species are found.

10b Front femora not as in 10a. 11

11a Tarsi with 3 segments. 12

11b Tarsi with but 2 segments*; body much flattened and very thin for living under bark. (Flat Bugs) See 14a and Fig. 221.

Family 5, ARADIDAE

The Flat Bugs have a four-segmented beak but in some the beak is apparently three-segmented; accordingly the family is repeated here.

12a Beak short and thick, not reaching the middle coxae; antennae thread-like at tip (rather rarely with 5 segments). Head narrow, its 2 ocelli when present back of eyes. (Assassin Bugs) Fig. 219.

Family 12, REDUVIIDAE

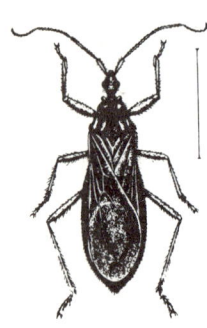

Figure 219

Fig. 219. *Redùvius personàtus* (L.)

Blackish brown; the knees, tarsi and apical half of the tibia paler. Known as the "masked bed-bug hunter" or "kissing bug." Some contend that the latter name belongs to a similar but blacker species (*Melanolestes pícipes.*) Both spécies may bite painfully if handled carelessly. They are frequently seen at lights. Length 17-20 mm. (From U.S.D.A.)

The bloodthirsty pirates composing this family live for the most part by catching and sucking the blood of other insects. Some attack man or other mammals. There are many species which vary widely in size and form. The thread-legged bug; long and slim and somewhat resembling a walking-stick, belongs here.

12b Beak longer. 13

13a With ocelli. 14

13b Broad, flat, flightless bugs; without ocelli. (Bed Bugs, etc.) Fig. 220.

Family 16, CIMICIDAE

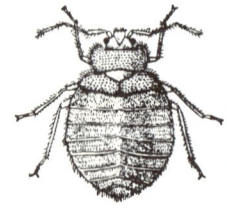

Figure 220

Fig. 220. *Cìmex lectulàrius* L.

The Bed Bug.

Dark reddish brown, sometimes yellowish. Wings very short and functionless. It hides by day but with the setting of the sun comes forth to make the night long to be remembered. Length 4-5 mm. (From U.S.D.A.)

This family is a small one, the bed bug being the only well known species. The others are parasites on bats and a few birds, but do not attack man.

⚘ A few members of the family Anthocoridae also have but 2 tarsal segments.

14a Front wing without closed cells but with a large embolium (A). (Tarsi sometimes with but two segments.) (Flower Bugs) Fig. 221.

Family 17, ANTHOCORIDAE

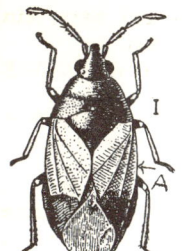

Figure 221

Fig. 221. *Triphleps insidiosus* (Say)

The Insidious Flower Bug. Black, shining, elytra pale yellowish. Length 1.8-2 mm. (U.S.D.A.)

This small family of small bugs is scattered world wide. They seem to be predaceous on mites and tiny insects. The species pictured is very common, often bites without provocation and "packs a wallop" unbelievably out of proportion to its size.

14b Front wing without an embolium but with 4 to 5 closed cells; ocelli between the eyes. (Shore Bugs) Fig. 222.

Family 26, SALDIDAE

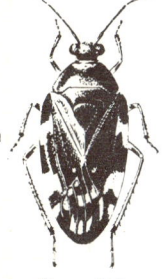

Figure 222

Fig. 222. *Saldula confluenta* (Say)

Black, shining with pale markings as pictured. Length 6mm. (after Sim).

The members of this small family frequent the shores of salt water and operate much like the tiger beetles, being very actively predaceous.

15a Front wings with a cuneus (C) and an embolium (narrow marginal area, E) Fig. 223. 16

15b Front wing with neither a cuneus or embolium. 17

Figure 223

16a Membrane of front wing with 1 or 2 closed cells (See Fig. 223A and B); no ocelli. (Plant Bugs) Fig. 224. Family 19, MIRIDAE

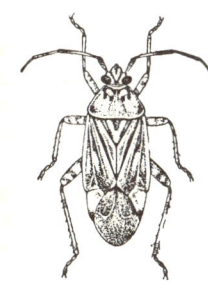

Figure 224

Fig. 224. *Lygus oblineatus* (Say) The Tarnished Plant Bug.

Dull reddish or brownish yellow marked with blackish; clavus and corium usually reddish brown Length 5-6 mm. (From U.S.D.A.)

This is one of the most common representatives of this large family. Plant bugs are very abundant throughout the summer. There is wide variation in their color, size and relative shapes. They are often very destructive.

16b Membrane without closed cells; ocelli sometimes present. (Tarsi sometimes but 2.) (Flower Bugs) (See 14α, Fig. 221).

Family 17, ANTHOCORIDAE

17α Front legs fitted for catching insect prey. Fig. 225. 18

17b Not preying on other insects. 19

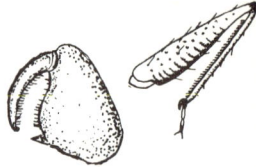

Figure 225

18α Front legs fitted with fine spines for catching small insects; head without transverse grooves. Usually slender insects. (Damsel Bugs) Fig. 226. Family 15, NABIDAE

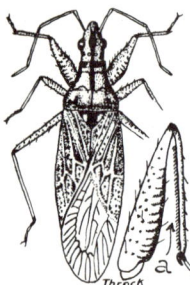

Figure 226

Fig. 226. *Nàbis térus* (L.)

Dull ashy gray or grayish yellow. Head and front of pronotum with median dark stripe. There are both short-winged and long-winged forms. This is one of several quite similar common species of this genus. Length 6-9 mm.

The Damsel bugs are more vicious than their name might indicate. They seem to feed largely on plant lice and other soft-bodied insects. The family is a small one.

18b Femur of front leg greatly thickened; tarsi reduced and obscure. (Beak in fact with 4 segments but usually only 3 apparent.) (Ambush Bugs) (See 10α, Fig. 218). Family 11, PHYMATIDAE

19α Tarsi with but 2 segments; much flattened and very thin for living under bark. (Flat Bugs) Fig. 227. Family 5, ARADIDAE

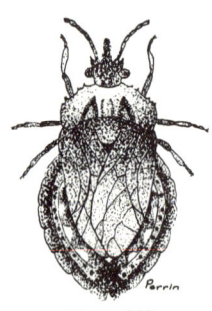

Figure 227

Fig. 227. *Áradus acùtus* Say

Blackish brown; a row of whitish spots on each side of exposed disk of abdomen and on elytra. Head longer than wide and longer than pronotum. Found under bark of logs. Length 7-10 mm.

The Flat bugs are well named. They live under bark and some of them have been reduced almost to the thinness of paper. The general color is black· or dark brown. Some species bear small markings of red or of white.

19b Tarsi with 3 segments; not flattened and very thin. 20

20a With ocelli. 21

20b Without ocelli; eyes large; 2 closed cells at base of wing membrane. (Red Bugs) Fig. 228.   Family 8, PYRRHOCORIDAE

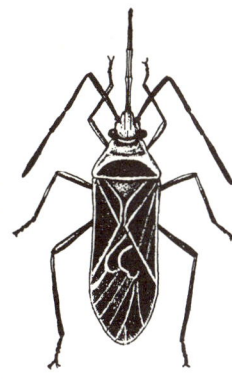

Figure 228

Fig. 228. *Dysdércus suturéllus* (H-S.)

The Cotton Stainer.

Bright to dull red. Length 12-17 mm.

This comparatively small family is made up of mostly gregarious plant feeding bugs. They range up to two inches in length.

As the names indicate these bugs are prominently marked with red. The species pictured is sometimes a serious pest in the cotton fields of our South. Several other species of this genus attack cotton in other parts of the world.

21a Body and appendages very slender; antennae longer than body. Its fourth segment short and thickened. (Stilt Bugs). Fig. 229,
Family 6, NEIDIDAE

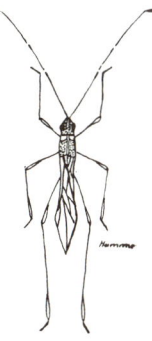

Figure 229

Fig. 229. *Jalýsus spinósus* (Say)

Dull reddish or yellowish brown. First joint of antennae longer than third, second only twice the length of fourth. Scutellum with spine inclined at angle of about 45 degrees. Length 7-9 mm.

The Stilt Bugs are very slender insects with long weak legs and antennae. They are fairly abundant and may be readily taken by sweeping. The family is a small one.

21b Body not extremely slender as in 21a; antennae shorter than body. 22

22a Membrane of front wing with many veins, usually forked. (α) (Squash Bug Family) Fig. 230. Family 4, COREIDAE

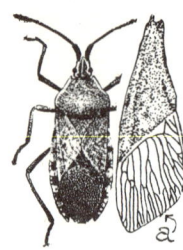

Figure 230

Fig. 230. *Ānasa trístis* (De Geer) The Squash Bug.

Depressed above. Dull brownish yellow, grayed with black punctures. Head black with three yellow lines. Alternate squares of black and yellow on connexivum (sides of abdomen). A serious pest of squashes and pumpkins. Length 13-18 mm. (From U.S.D.A.)

Most of the members of this large family are plant feeders. They are provided for defense with stink glands with which they make their neighborhood hideous when disturbed. They vary greatly in shape and color. They are medium to large bugs.

22b Membrane of front wing with but four or five veins (A). (Some species with short winged or wingless forms; B) (Cinch-bug Family.) Fig. 231. Family 7, LYGAEIDAE

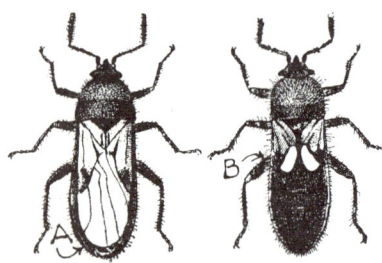

Figure 231

Fig. 231. *Blissus leucópterus* (Say) The Chinch Bug.

Dull black, thickly covered with fine pubescence. Elytra white with large black spot on corium. Legs and beak brownish yellow. Length about 4 mm. (From U.S.D.A.)

The Chinch bug alone would make this large family famous but many other notable pests belong here also. They are mostly plant feeders. Many are small. Some are wingless. Young collectors frequently discard these short winged forms for nymphs.

23a Without ocelli; living in water though often found flying around lights. 24

23b With ocelli; head much wider than long; live on damp freshwater shores. (Toad Bugs) Fig. 232.

Family 31, GELASTOCÓRIDAE

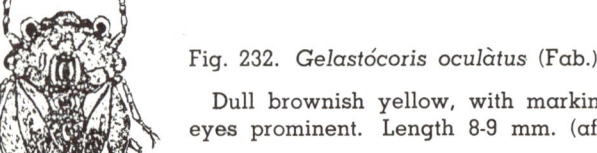

Figure 232

Fig. 232. *Gelastócoris oculàtus* (Fab.)

Dull brownish yellow, with markings of darker; eyes prominent. Length 8-9 mm. (after Luggers).

The members of this small family live a predaceous life on banks of water courses. Most of the limited number of species are confined to tropical América.

24a Hind tarsi with claws, front legs for catching prey. 25
24b Hind tarsi without distinct claws, front legs not especially modified for catching prey. 27
25a Membrane of front wing plainly veined. 26
25b Head wider than long; membrane of front wing without distinct veins. (Water Creepers) Fig. 233.   Family 28, NAUCÓRIDAE

Fig. 233. *Pelócoris femorátus* (PdeB)

Greenish brown with markings of whitish and dull yellow. Length 9-12 mm.

The members of this family live in quiet shallow water. They are predaceous on the animal life of their world.

Figure 233

26a Hind legs flattened for swimming. Large oval insects. (Giant Water Bugs) Fig. 234.   Family 30, BELOSTÓMIDAE

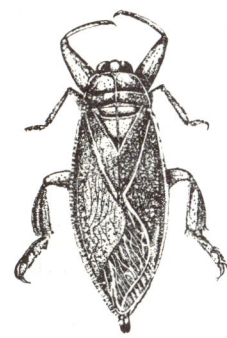

Fig. 234. *Benácus gríseus* (Say)

Dull yellowish brown. Front femora rounded in front not to receive tibiae. *Lethócerus americànus,* a similar species is distinguished by such grooves. Length 50-55 mm. (Kan. SBA.)

Some members of this family are truly giant and never fail to attract popular interest. They are predaceous. Young fish, tadpoles, and other water insects suffer heavily that these insects may live. There are but a few species. The female of some species glues her eggs to the back of the male which must then carry them about until they hatch. Specimens thus bearing eggs always attract attention.

Figure 234

26b Hind legs for walking. Mostly long slim insects. (Water Scorpions) Fig. 235.   Family 29, NÉPIDAE

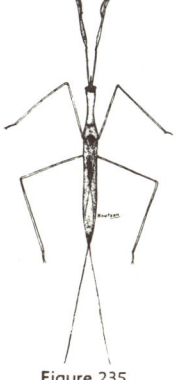

Fig. 235. *Ránatra fúsca* P. B.

Dark reddish to fuscous brown; legs but faintly annulated if at all. Front part of pronotum less than half the width of hind part. Length of body 35-42 mm.

The members of the genus *Nèpa* are broad and flat, roughly resembling the giant water bugs, but have a long respiratory tube at the end of the abdomen. Members of the genus *Ránata* are much more common. They seem to prefer shallow stagnant water. If one will rake out the decaying vegatation on the bank, these interesting insects may be separated from it. They are predacious.

Figure 235

27a Front tarsi of but one scoop-shaped segment and without claws, mouth opening wide, "beak" very short (A); body flattened above with head over-lapping the thorax dorsally. (Water Boatmen) Fig. 236. Family 33, **CORÍXIDAE**

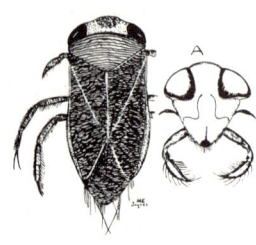

Figure 236

Fig. 236. *Arctocorixa interrúpta* (Say)

Above brown, hind angle of pronotum obtuse; pronotum marked with transverse black lines. The median ones usually interrupted. Perhaps our most common species. Abundant in streams and flying at lights. Length 10-11 mm.

The Water Boatmen swim on their ventral surface as would be expected, instead of on their back as do the *Notonéctidae*. They seem to live on the minute plant and animal life in the ooze which they shovel into their short tube-like mouths with their front legs. The posterior pair of legs is held in the position of and used like oars when they swim.

27b Front tarsi with claws, body convex above with head inserted into the thorax. (Back Swimmers). Fig. 237. Family 27, **NOTONÉCTIDAE**

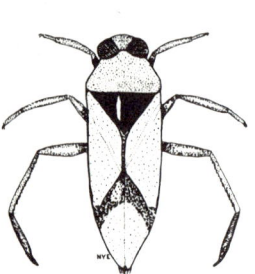

Figure 237

Fig. 237. *Notonécta undulàta* Say

Dull yellowish white, usually marked with black. Often abundant in stagnant pools. Care should be taken in handling; they bite viciously. Length 10-12 mm.

As the name indicates, the members of this family swim with their backs down. The body is boat shaped and stream lined. It is the hind pair of legs that are used for swimming. They often hang head down at the surface of the water, with the tip of the abdomen exposed to secure air. They are highly predacious and are known to kill young fish considerably larger than themselves.

ORDER HOMÓPTERA

1a Large insects with broad head, clear wings; three ocelli; front
femora thickened. (The Cicadas or so called "Locusts") Fig. 238.

Family 1. CICADIDAE

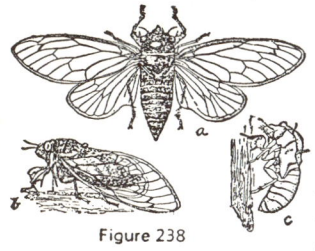

Fig. 238. *Magicicàda septéndecim* (L.)
Periodical or Seventeen Year Cicada.

Head, thorax, and abdomen mostly
black; veins of wings and some markings
on body orange brown; eyes red. The
adults of these interesting insects mature
and appear in May for about six weeks

Figure 238

of activity once each seventeen years. It
should be noted, however, that there are seventeen broods so that
adults appear somewhere every year and some localities may have
two or more visits in a seventeen year period due to overlapping
broods. Throughout the South there are thirteen broods which have
a thirteen year cycle. Length to tip of wings 35-45 mm. (From U.S.D.A.)

There are about 200 N. Am. species of Cicadas and 1500 for the
whole world. One in Borneo is 3 inches long.

1b Smaller insects, seldom over one-half inch long; only two ocelli
or none. 2

2a Tarsi three jointed, antennae bristle like, inconspicuous, beak
plainly arising from head. 3

2b Tarsi one or two jointed; antennae threadlike, conspicuous or absent; beak apparently arising from between front legs. 6

3a Antennae arising from side of head
below the eyes (a, Fig. 239); ocelli below or near the eyes. (Lanternflies)
Fig. 240.

Figure 239

Family 5. FULGÓRIDAE

Fig. 240. A, Scòlops súlcipes Say
Brown. Common in meadows
and weedy places. Length 9-11
mm. B, Órmensis pruinòsa Say
Gray marked with black. Length
8 mm.

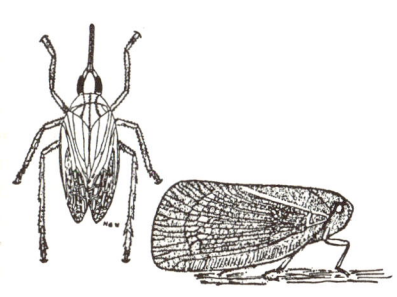

Figure 240

Our members of this family
vary widely in appearance. Members of the genus *Scolops* are common in pastures and wherever
grass grows. Some of the other
genera have broad green or
brown wings and in shape resemble moths. The family is a
fairly large one.

117

3b Antennae arising in front of the eyes and between them (a, Fig. 241). 4

Figure 241

4a Prothorax extending back over the abdomen; insect usually widest in front; frequently with a horn or horns on the thorax. (Treehoppers) Fig. 242. Family 3, MEMBRACIDAE

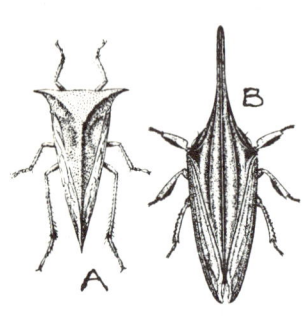

Figure 242

Fig. 242. A, *Cerèsa bubàlus* Fab. The Buffalo Treehopper. Light green to brownish, 6-7 mm. B, *Campylénchia látipes* Say. Reddish brown, 6-8 mm. (Kan. S.B.A.)

Professor Comstock has aptly suggested that "Nature must have been in a joking mood when she made the treehoppers". They are surely a grotesque lot of little creatures with their curiously distorted prothorax. Some species doubtless get some good protection through their resemblance to thorns as they stand head down on the stems of plants. They do not have a 100% faith in the program for when disturbed move around to the opposite side of the stem, — a queer thing for "thorns" to do.

4b Prothorax not as in 4a. 5
5a Hind tibiae with rowed spines on under side. (Leaf-hoppers) Fig. 243. Family 4, CICADELLIDAE

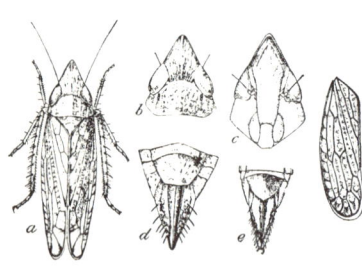

Figure 243

Fig. 243. *Platymetòpius acùtus* Say

The Sharp-nosed Leafhopper. (a, Adult; b, vertex and pronotum; c, face; d, female genitalia; e, male genitalia; f, elytron.)

Brown, often with bronze lustre. Face yellow, bordered with brown. Length about 5 mm. (From U.S.D.A.)

This is the largest family of homoptera. They are slender, mostly sharp-nosed, quick jumping little insects. They are often exceedingly abundant and do much damage to plants. Many species have two host plants and make regular seasonal migrations from one to the other.

5b Hind tibiae without spines except at end which has several small spines and one or two large teeth. (Spittle Insects or Frog Hoppers.) Fig. 244.

Family 2, CERCÓPIDAE

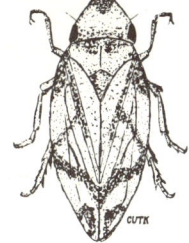

Figure 244

Fig. 244. *Lepyrónia quadrangulàris* (Say)

Dusky-gray to deep tawny-brown. Spots darker shades of ground color. Length 6-8 mm.

The nymphs of the spittle insects hide themselves in a mass of foam which is often on a stem in the axils of the leaves. Birds presumably do not think or care to probe into this frothy mass when in search of food. The adults which develop within this protection are shaped somewhat like leafhoppers but are usually broader.

6a Hind legs fitted for leaping with thick femora. Antennae nine or ten jointed. Front wings often leathery. (Jumping Plant Lice) Fig. 245.

Family 6, CHÉRMIDAE

Figure 245

Fig. 245. *Psýlla pyrícola* Foerster The Pear Psylla.

Dark reddish brown, the abdomen banded with black. An enemy of the pear. Length 2-3 mm. (From U.S.D.A.)

These are tiny insects that look like miniature cicadas. They live on the limbs and twigs of plants and may cause severe damage. Some are gall makers. The family is not a large one.

6b Not as in 6a. 7

7a Legless, wingless, scale or mealy covered insects living and often firmly attached on limbs of plants (females), or without beak, and with legs with but one tarsal joint, one pair of wings and long antennae (males). (Scale Insects, Bark Lice, Mealy Bugs, etc.) Fig. 246.

Family 9, CÓCCIDAE

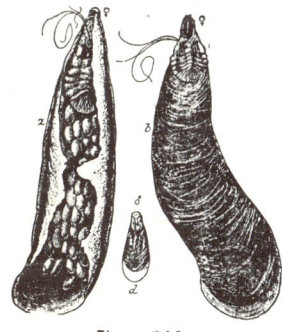

Figure 246

Fig. 246. *Lepidósaphes úlmi* (L.) The Oystershell Scale. (a, Female with eggs; b, mature female; d, male.)

Scale dark brown to black. The young are yellowish, and active for a short time after hatching. One of our most common scales on fruit trees and shrubs. Length; female about 3 mm. Male about 1mm.

This is a fairly large family of highly destructive insects. The males usually have one pair of wings, and the young run about actively for a short time. Other than this, the usual procedure is to thrust the sucking tube into the tissue of the plant host, build a waxen scale over the tiny body and spend the entire life in the one spot. Fruit and shade trees and greenhouse and house plants are frequently heavily damaged.

7b Not as in 7a. **8**

8a Wings opaque, usually whitish, sometimes with colored markings; body and wings covered with white powder; tarsi with two segments. (Whiteflies.) Fig. 247. Family 8, ALEYRÓDIDAE

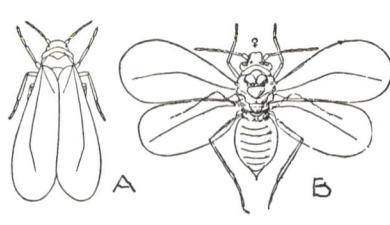

Figure 247

Fig. 247. A, *Trialeuròdes vaporiorum* (West.); The Greenhouse Whitefly; B, *Dialeuórdes cítri* (Ashm.) The Citris Whitefly.

Whiteflies are from 1 to 3 mm. long with body and four wings of both sexes covered with white powder. The nymphs resemble the scale insects. Provokingly destructive to many plants in greenhouses and out of doors.

Some species of Whiteflies show colors on the body and black spots on the wings. They are always small and may multiply very rapidly.

8b Wings when present transparent (sometimes colored) legs long and slender. (Plant Lice or Aphids) Fig. 248. Family 7, APHÍDIDAE

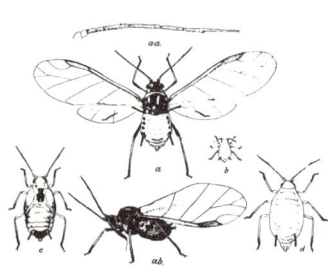

Figure 248

Fig. 248. *Àphis gossýpii* Glover

The Melon Aphid (a and ab, Winged forms; c, wingless female; b, and d, nymphs; aa, antenna.)
Greenish to jet black. Feeds on many plants but particularly destructive to cucumbers and melons where it feeds on the underside of leaves causing them to curl and die. Length 2-3 mm. (From U.S.D.A.)

Aphids are very numerous. Almost every species of plant is attacked by them. Many species pass through the winter as eggs from which only females hatch. These in turn give birth to living young. Many generations follow thus throughout the summer. All are females. Many have no wings but some generations are in part or wholly winged. These hunt new feeding grounds and often regularly migrate to a wholly different species of plant, and have a seasonal alternation between two hosts. Ants may frequently be seen caring for aphids, from which they get honey dew.

ORDER NEURÓPTERA

1a Prothorax long and slender (a); front legs greatly enlarged (b) **and** fitted for grasping. (Mantis-like Neuroptera) Fig. 249.

Family 3, MANTÍSPIDAE

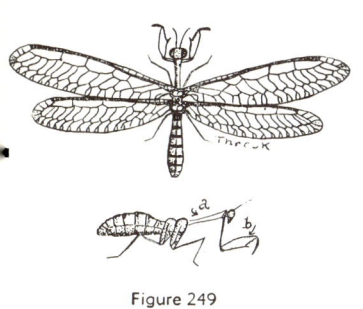

Figure 249

Fig. 249. *Mantíspa interrúpta.* Say

Greenish brown to brown. Markings on wings brown. Length of body 17-20 mm. Expanse of wings about 40 mm.

The few representatives of this family are such unusual creatures that when the collector takes his first specimen, he is likely to feel that he is dreaming. The prothorax is elongated giving the appearance of a long slim neck. The front legs are large and fitted for grasping prey.

A few western "Snakeflies", belonging to the family Raphidìidae, differ from the Mantispids in having slender front legs.

1b Not as in 1a. 2

2a Base of hind wing broad, anal area folded fanlike when at rest. (Alderflies, Dobsonflies and Fishflies) (Fig. 250.

Family 1, SIÁLIDAE

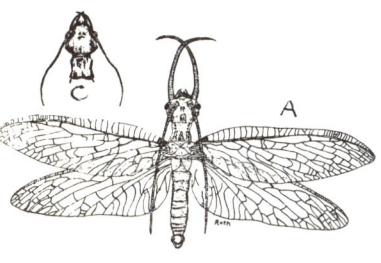

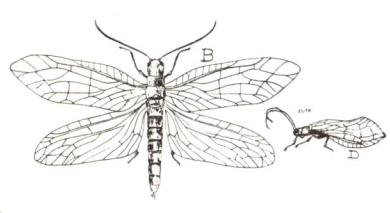

Figure 250

Fig. 250, A. *Corydalus cornùtus* L. Dobsonfly.

Brown, the sexes differ in that the male has long mandibles and the female short ones (C). They are found flying near streams and attract much attention. Wing expanse 100-130 mm.

250B. *Siàlis infumàta* Newm. The Smoky Alderfly.

Body black; wings brownish black. Wing expanse 25-30 mm. D, wings folded.

This family contains the largest members of the Neuroptera. The larvae are aquatic, and the adults ordinarily do not get far from water. The alderflies are comparatively small, soft winged and often smoke colored. Some systematists make two families of this group.

2b Hind wings narrow at base, not folded. ....3■

3a Less than one inch in length; antennae not enlarged at tip......4

3b Over an inch in length; antennae short and usually knobbed at end. 5

4a The radius of fore wing with at least three rather parallel branches as pictured. The adults are longer than the preceding and in smaller than the lacewings. (Brown Lacewings) Fig. 251.
Family 6, HEMEROBIIDAE

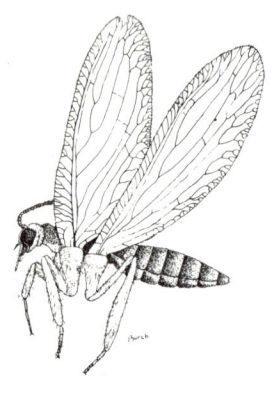

Figure 251

Fig. 251. *Hemeròbius stigmatéris* Fitch Brownish. Length to top of folded wings 10 mm.

This family though not large is widely distributed. The members are small lacewings usually brown in color. The eggs are attached directly to their support and not put on thread-supports as in the following family. The larvae are predaceous on scale insects and aphids and have been called aphis wolves.

4b The radius of fore wing with but one zig-zag longitudinal branch as pictured. The adults are larger than the preceding and in life are green or yellowish green with golden eyes. (Lacewings or Aphis Lions) Fig. 252.
Family 9, CHRYSÓPIDAE

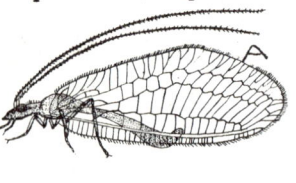

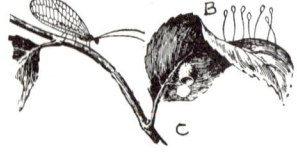

Figure 252

Fig. 252. *Chrysòpa oculàta* Say; B, eggs. C, pupa case.

Living, pale green with golden eyes; pinned specimens, greenish yellow to brown. Length to tip of wings 12-17 mm.

This is a large and widely distributed family. The eggs are placed on the ends of slender hair-like supports, apparently to prevent the first larvae to hatch from eating the remaining eggs. Their ravenous larvae are known as Aphis Lions.

5a Antennae long. Insects resembling dragonflies except for antennae. (Ascalaphids) Fig. 253. Family 11, ASCALAPHIDAE

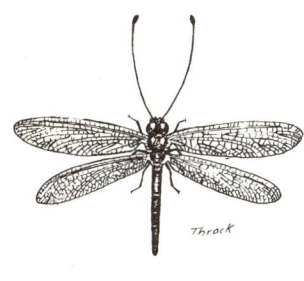

Figure 253

Fig. 253. *Ulolodes macleayana hageni* Van der Weele.

Reddish brown. Long lighter brown hairs on front of head and sides of thorax. Wings hyaline. Stigma near apex of wings, yellowish white. Expanse of wings about 65 mm.

If it had not been a rather innocent little girl who brought in my first specimen of this family I would have been sure it had been made by gluing parts of different insects together. The Ascalaphids are not at all common. The adults prey on other insects.

5b Antennae short. Feeble flying insects, resembling damselflies. (Ant Lions) Fig. 254. Family 10, MYRMELEONIDAE

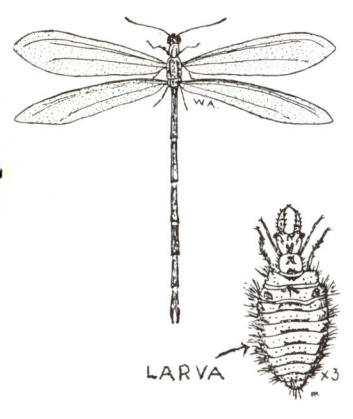

LARVA x3

Figure 254

Fig. 254. *Hesperoleon abdominalis* (Say)

Pronotum yellow with a pair of dorso-lateral brown bands; abdomen dark; labrum yellow; tibial spurs slightly curved. Spread of wings about 45 mm. Length about 40 mm.

This is the family of the far famed "doodle bug." The larva makes a funnel-shaped pit in dry sand or soil in a protected place, then lies buried at the bottom of its trap waiting for some passing ant to slide down the "funnel's" side. As the story goes they may be called up into view by repeating "Doodle-doodle-doodle." It should be remarked, however, that the performance must be entered into with such enthusiasm that some sand or other particles are blown or knocked down the side of the trap, then the "doodle bug" comes out to catch the ant it would normally find.

ORDER TRICHÓPTERA

1a Maxillary palpi with 5 segments. **2**

1b Maxillary palpi with but three segments in males (♀, 5). Front tibiae with but one spur. Fig. 255.

Family 12, LIMNEPHÍLIDAE

Fig. 255. *Hálesus* sp.

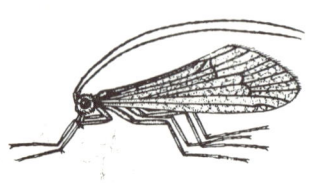

Figure 255

The larvae of these interesting and often highly abundant insects are caddis-worms. They live in streams and lakes and employ a wide variation of building materials from which to construct the protective case or tube in which they live. The foundation is silk to which tiny stones, sticks, etc. are attached. Species found living in quiet waters may be reared in an aquarium and their habits observed.

2a With ocelli; antennae very long; body thickly clothed with hairs. Fig. 256. Family 10, LEPTOCERIDAE

Fig. 256. *Leptócerus* sp.

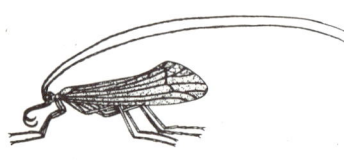

Figure 256

The larvae of this family as with most caddisflies are vegetable feeders. It is this work of converting plants into acceptable fish food that makes the order important to the conservationist.

2b Without ocelli; fore tibiae with two spurs; middle and hind tibiae with four spurs each. Fig. 257. Family 4, HYDROPSÝCHIDAE

Fig. 257. *Macronèma zebrátum* Hagen

Reddish brown marked with whitish. Length to tip of wings 12-18 mm.

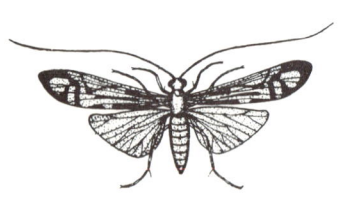

Figure 257

This large family is world wide in its distribution. They are known as the Seine-making Caddis-flies from their way of building tiny nets across currents of flowing water. The minute plant and animal life thus caught constitutes their food.

ORDER LEPIDÓPTERA

1a Antennae bearing a knob or club at the end. 2

1b Antennae of varying shapes but not knobbed at end. 8

2a Antennae close together at bases and without recurved hook at end of knob; front wing with less than five branches arising from top of discal cell; body slender. (Butterflies) 3

2b Antennae wide apart at bases and usually with a recurved hook (A) at end of knob; front wing with five branches arising from top of discal cell, body frequently heavy. (The Skippers) Fig. 258.

Family 9, HESPERIIDAE

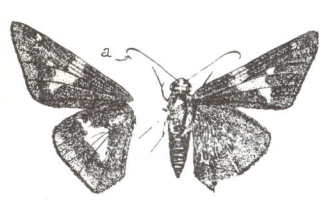

Figure 258

Fig. 258. *Epargýreus títyrus* Fabr.

The Silver Spotted Skipper.

Dark chocolate brown with yellowish spots. Large irregular silvery white spot in center on under side of back wings. Expanse of wings about 50 mm.

This family represents a half-way condition between the moths and the butterflies. Active by day; — some are so completely 50-50 that when at rest they hold the front wings erect like butterflies and spread the back ones like the moths. Their caterpillars present a curious appearance with large heads supported by very slender necks.

3a Large butterflies usually with tail like projection (a) extending back from hind wings. (The Swallow-tails) Fig. 258.

Family 1, PAPILIÓNIDAE

Figure 259

Fig. 259. *Papílio àjax* L.

The Black Swallowtail.

Ground color black; markings of yellow. Many blue scales between the two rows of yellow spots on back wings; more in female. Orange spot with black center near anal angle of back wing. The beautiful yellow and black caterpillar feeds on the leaves of carrots and related plants. Expanse of wing from 90 to 115 mm. (From U.S.D.A.)

The swallowtail butterflies are so named from the tail like prolongations on the hind wings. They are all of large size. The caterpillars have no spines but project a pair of fleshy horns from the prothorax when disturbed. These horns emit an unpleasant odor.

3b Not as in 3a. **4**

4a Front legs, especially of males reduced in size and not used for walking; claws if present not divided. **5**

4b Front legs normal and used for walking (if reduced in size the claws are toothed or divided). Medium size; yellow, white, or orange wings often marked with black. (Pierids.) Fig. 260.

Family 2, **PIÉRIDAE**

Fig. 260. *Pieris rápae* (L.) The Imported Cabbageworm.

White, marked with black. The one shown is a female. The males have but one black dot on each front wing. The larva is the well known velvety green caterpillar found on cabbage and related plants. Expanse of wings 35-50 mm. (From U.S.D.A.)

Figure 260

The members of this family are mostly of medium size. They are white, yellow or orange. The wing margins are often decorated in black. They are common everywhere and are often seen in great numbers around mud holes, where they are getting water.

5a Front legs in both sexes reduced in size and folded against the thorax; male tarsi with but one segment, female with five segments; tarsi without claws. **6**

5b Front legs of female with two claws and used normally. Small or medium size; blue, violet, or brown, sometimes with small red markings or tiny tail like projections. (Gossamer-winged Butterflies.) Fig. 261.

Family 8, **LYCÁENIDAE**

Fig. 261. *Heòdes thòe* Bdv.

The Bronze Copper Butterfly.

Front wings orange copper with dark border. Back wings purplish brown with border of reddish copper. Expanse of wings 34-38 mm.

These butterflies are small and delicate. The wings are daintily marked; brilliant shades of blue and copper are common.

Figure 261

6a Front legs of females with a knob at end; antennae without scales or nearly so. Large reddish and black or brown butterflies; larvae feed on milkweed. (Milkweed Butterflies.) Fig. 262.

Family 3, DANAIDAE

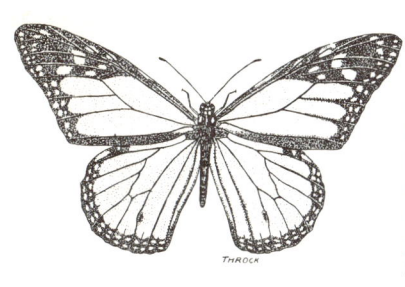

Figure 262

Fig. 262. *Danaus plexippus* (L.)

The Monarch Butterfly.

Ground color of wings brownish red; their borders and veins black. White spots in border. Males may be distinguished by scent pouch on a vein of back wing. The pale yellowish caterpillar, marked with rings of black, feeds on milkweed. Expanse of wings about 100 mm.

The Monarch is one of our best known butterflies. It collects in large numbers in the fall and migrates to the South. It seems that none spends the winter here but that each spring they return from the warmer South, to lay their eggs and get things going again.

6b Antennae clothed at least in part with scales. 7

7a Discal cell of back wings closed by a prominent vein. (Meadowbrowns) Fig. 263.

Family 4, SATYRIDAE

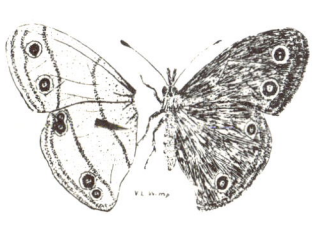

Figure 263

Fig. 263. *Cissia eurytus* Fabr.

The Little Wood-satyr.

Upper surface dark brown, outer fourth sometimes paler. Spots black with pale yellow margins. Expanse of wings 35-40 mm.

These are, for the most part, medium-sized brown butterflies. They have a row of rather prominent eye spots along the outer margin of the wing. They are frequently found in open woods and meadows.

7b Discal cell of back wings either open (A) or closed by a mere vestige of a vein. (Nymphs) Fig. 264.   Family 5, NYMPHÁLIDAE

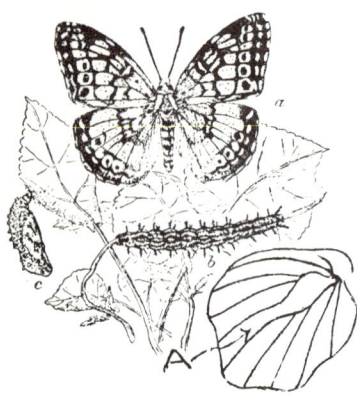

Figure 264

Fig. 264. *Euptoièta claúdia* Cram.

The Variegated Fritillary.

Wings reddish brown with pale cross band and dark markings. The caterpillar is orange red with dark stripes and whitish blotches. It bears six rows of spines. Expanse of wings 45-65 mm. (From U.S.D.A.)

These butterflies are medium to large size and are alike in having the front legs greatly reduced in size in both sexes. This is our largest family of butterflies.

8a Wings wholly or in large part transparent, without scales; slender moths that resemble bees. (Clear-wings) Fig. 265.
Family 45, AEGERIIDAE

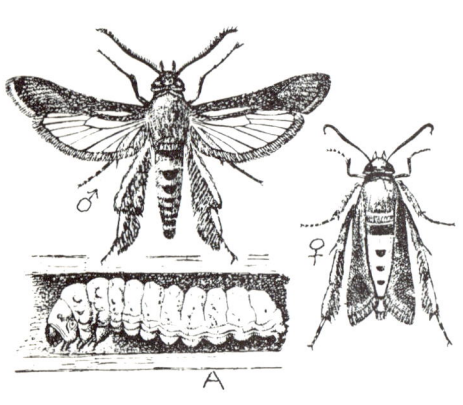

Figure 265

Fig. 265. *Melíttia cucúrbitae* (Harr.) The Squash Borer.

Fore wings, thorax, and basal segment of abdomen, dark metallic green. The remainder of abdomen and leg red, marked with black. The larvae bore in joints of squash v i n e s, destroying them (A). Hind wings clear. Expanse of wings about 35 mm. (From U.S.D.A.)

The clear wing moths are beautiful bee-like insects that love the sunlight and fly rapidly by day. The larvae do not have a proper regard for man's possessions. They bore in many of his trees and herbaceous plants, greatly to their hurt. Some Sphinx moths have wings partly transparent and might erroneously be placed here.

8b Wings fully covered with scales. (If partly transparent the antennae thicker near tip than at base). 9

9a Rather small moths with wings split lengthwise, the borders of these segments fringed with scales. (Plume-moths) Fig. 266.
Family 37, PTEROPHÓRIDAE

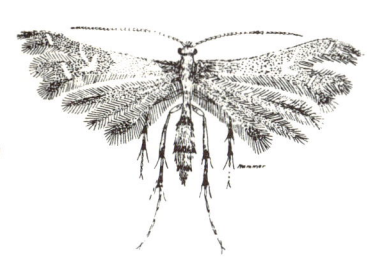

Figure 266

Fig. 266. *Pteróphorus perischelidáctylus* Fitch. The Grape Plume Moth.

Yellowish brown marked with whitish. Wing margins bordered with fringe of whitish scales. The caterpillars are greenish with white hairs. Expanse of wing 17-20 mm.

These moths have their wings split into feather-like parts, hence the name. The front wings have two or three parts, the hind wings being split into three or four parts. The "plumes" overlap when the moths are at rest, giving them an odd appearance. The family is a small one; the moths are also small.

Family 38, ORNEÓDIDAE includes small silvery-white moths which have their wings divided into six segments.

9b Wings not split lengthwise. 10

10a Very small moths with narrow pointed wings; hind margins of wings with wide fringe of scales. (Tineids) Fig. 267.
Family 62, TINEIDAE

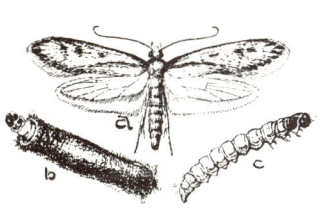

Figure 267

Fig. 267. *Tínea pellionélla* L.

The Casemaking Clothes Moth. (a, Adult Moth; b, larva in case; c, larva.)

The head and fore wings buff or grayish yellow; dimly spotted with darker. Hind wings whitish. The larva lives in clothing and furs and weaves a case about itself from the chewings of the fabric on which it feeds. An interesting experiment is to confine some of these larvae in a small tin box and change the color of the goods given them from time to time. They then weave a variegated case and one can tell in which order the different parts were put on. Expanse of wings 12-16 mm. (From U.S.D.A.)

This is a large family of mostly tiny moths, many of which are destructive. Many of the leaf miners belong here.

10b Wings not as in 10a. 11

11a Small or very small, often bright colored moths; hind wing often pointed at apex and broader than front wing. Larvae leaf miners, leaf rollers, seed feeders, etc. Fig. 268.

Family 40, GELECHIIDAE

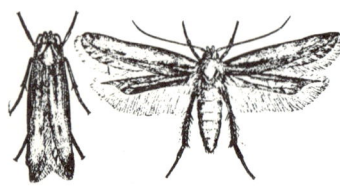

Figure 268

Fig. 268. *Sitotroga cerealella* (Olivier)

The Angoumois Grain Moth.

Pale yellow, expanding 20-25 mm.

This large family has about 4000 species scattered everywhere. Many are destructive pests. An interesting elongated gall common on golden-rod stems is made by one of these moths (a spherical goldenrod gall is made by a fly.)

11b Not as in 11a. 12

12a Narrow strong wings; front ones considerably longer than back wings; heavy spindle-shaped body. 13

12b Not with the combination of characters in 12a. 14

13a Antennae pectinate (occasionally simple in the female); proboscis absent; front wing with accessory cell (A). Larvae live within the wood of trees. (Carpenter Moths). Fig. 269.

Family 63, COSSIDAE

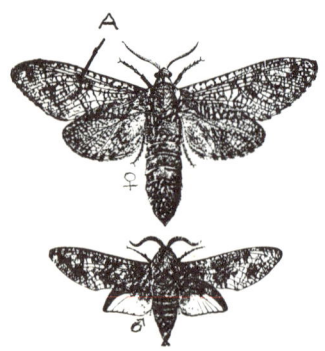

Figure 269

Fig. 269. *Prionoxystus robiniae* (Peck)

The Carpenterworm. ♀ mottled gray; ♂ darker gray, back wings prominently marked with vermilion. Wing expanse 50-90 mm.

This rather small family bore as lar-vae in the trunks and branches of our deciduous trees and may be very de-structive. The adults are often seen at lights. They range throughout the broad leaf tree belts of North America.

13b Antennae often prism-shaped; tapering at both ends, sometimes hooked at end; usually large moths. The hind wings of some species partly or wholly transparent.

Family 10, **SPHINGIDAE**

Fig. 270. *Protoparce sexta* Johan.

The Tobacco Hornworm. (a, Adult; b, larva; c, pupa, frequently spaded up in gardens.)

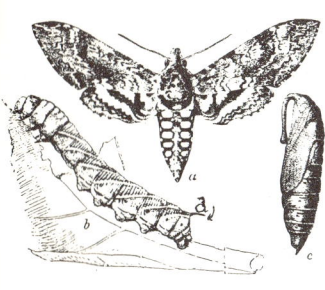

Figure 270

Wings brownish gray, marked with black, brown and whitish lines and spots. Abdomen gray and black with two rows of large yellow spots. The larvae feed on tomato and tobacco. Expanse of wings 100-130 mm. Our sphinx moths are medium to large size and are narrow winged, swift flyers. Many of the larvae have a horn (a) at the posterior end. It is harmless. (From U.S.D.A.)

14a Small, feebly flying, smoke colored moths with long, narrow, thinly scaled wings and slender, plumose antennae; often marked with yellow or red. (Smoky Moths) Fig. 271.

Family 34, **ZYGAENIDAE**

Fig. 271. *Harrisina americàna* Guer.

The Grape-leaf Skeletonizer.

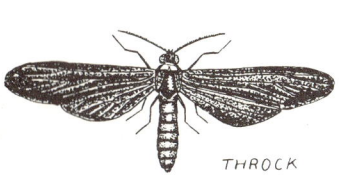

THROCK

Figure 271

Irridescent bluish or greenish black with bright yellow collar. The caterpillars feed in companies on the leaves of Virginia creeper and grape. Expanse of wings about 35 mm.

This is a small family of small moths. Most of them have smoky wings. Some have markings of bright colors.

14b Not as in 14a. **15**

15a The subcosta (S) and the radius (R) of the back wings are separate over the discal cell, then unite or run very close together, and then again separate (A). Mostly fairly small moths, some medium size; often straw-colored or brownish. (Superfamily PYRALIDOIDAE) Fig. 272. 16

Fig. 272. Hind wings of two typical members of the super family showing the characters used in the key.

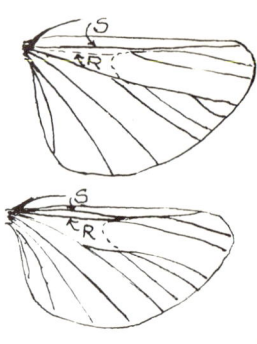

Figure 272

This group is large and includes many highly important economic pests. We follow McDunnough's check list for families and their arrangement. Many systematists would take two important groups out of his family *Pyrálidae* and give them family significance. In an effort to be consistent and yet help "beginners to begin", we are keying these three groups as subfamilies in keeping with the check list.

15b Not as in 15a. 18

16a Hind wings with fringe of long hairs along the vein below discal cell; labial palpi long and projecting forward forming a "snout"; wings wrapped around body when at rest. (Snout Moths, Sod Webworms) Fig. 273.   Subfamily CRÁMBINAE

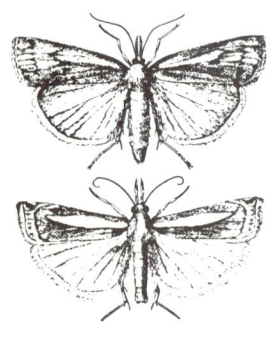

Figure 273

Fig. 273. A, *Crámbus mutàbilis* Clem.

The Striped Sod Webworm; B, *Crámbus praefectéllus* Zinck. The Silver-striped Webworm. (U.S.D.A.)

The members of this sub-family are all too common on the roots of grass plants where they live in webbed burrows by day and come out at night to "graze". The plants are sometimes cut off at the level of the ground. They are particularly annoying in this way when they get into fields of corn just coming up.

16b Hind wings without fringe and not wrapped around body as in 16a. 17

17a Maxillary palpi small, slender; fifth branch of radial vein of front wing (R5) arising from discal cell, as pictured. Fig. 274.

Subfamily PYRAUSTINAE

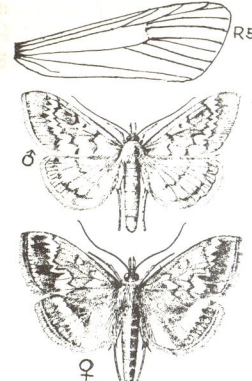

Fig. 274. *Pyrausta nubilalis* Hubner.

The European Corn Borer.

Light tan with brownish markings. The larva bores in stalks of corn and many other plants and has become a pest of major importance east of the Missouri river. Spread of wings 25-30 mm. (U.S.D.A.)

The sub-family includes many destructive species that feed on leaves and fruit of plants.

Figure 274

17b Maxillary palpi large; fifth branch of radial vein of front wing arising beyond the discal cell (A). Fig. 275.

Subfamily PYRALINAE

Fig. 275. *Pyralis farinalis* L.

The Meal Moth.

Golden yellow marked with reddish brown. Wing expanse 15 mm. (U.S.D.A.)

This is another large subfamily. They feed very largely on plants and so become ready pests when man attempts to store his products of the fields.

Figure 275

The Indian-meal Moth and the Mediterranean Flour Moth are common and exceedingly destructive pests and numerous other species take their toll in the pantry and warehouse. Some would include these in still another family or subfamily.

The so-called Cactus Moth works for us. When millions of acres in Australia had been over-run with cactus the moth was brought in from Argentina (1925) and made it much easier to bring the cactus under control.

The beginner could become easily confused in studying large groups like this superfamily, for systematists propose various arrangements some quite contradictory of others. Each one is attempting to show the true relationship as he sees it. After all,—our classification arrangements are only means to an end. Successful work with such great numbers of anything would be quite impossible if some orderly arrangement were not employed.

18a Larvae live within a silken bag covered with bits of little stems from the tree or other plant on which it feeds. Males as pictured; no proboscis; females do not leave the bag but deposit their eggs within it and die. (Bagworms) Fig. 276.

Family 29, PSYCHIDAE

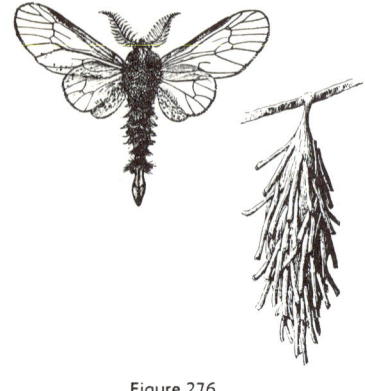

Figure 276

Fig. 276. *Thyridópteryx ephemeraefórmis* (Haw.) The Bagworm.

Black. Length 25 mm. (U.S.D.A.)

This is a relatively large and widely scattered family but since the females do not leave the "bag" their rate of spreading into new territory is slow. Eggs are laid in the bag where in most species they pass the winter. In the spring when the food plant has produced leaves the eggs hatch. The young caterpillars then build a case and live in it enlarging it all the while of course. The males are winged as pictured.

18b Larvae not living in bags or otherwise as in 18a. 19

19a Very large broad-winged, heavy-bodied moths. Many with transparent windows or eye spots (a) in wings; often with feathery antennae. (Royal Moths and Giant Silk-worm Moths. Fig. 277.

Family 11, SATURNIIDAE

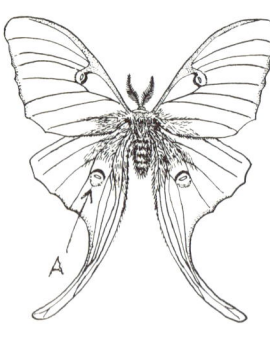

Figure 277

Fig. 277. *Tropáea lùna* L. The Luna Moth.

Wings delicate, light green; front margin of front wing brownish purple. Each wing has a transparent eye spot. Body and legs white. This is thought by many to be our most beautiful moth. Expanse of wings 75-90 mm.

The Giant Silk-worm moths have heavy bodies and hairy wings. They have feathery antennae, those of the males being broader than those of the females. The wings frequently have transparent window-like spots. The larvae feed on the leaves of different species of trees but are not ordinarily of sufficient abundance to do serious damage.

LEPIDOPTERA

19b Not as in 19a. 20

20a Front wings broad and usually ending squarely (somewhat rec-
angular in outline). Usually rather small tan, brownish of gray
moths not spreading much over an inch. (Leaf Rollers) Fig. 278.
Family 47, TORTRICIDAE

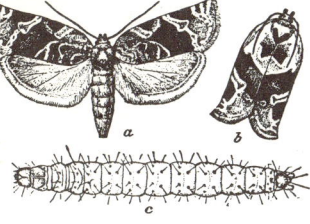

Figure 278

Fig. 278. *Argyrotaènia velùtinana*
(Wlk.) The Red-banded Leaf Roller.

Brownish with broad red band and
light markings. Wing expanse 15
mm. (U.S.D.A.)

The caterpillars of this fairly large
and widely scattered family usually
roll leaves into hollow cylinders with
their webs and live inside this protection. Many fruit and other trees
suffer from them. One can usually tell the adults at once by the shape
of the front wing.

20b Wings and otherwise not as in 20a. 21

21a Vein running along lower side of discal cell
of front wing, with three branches. (a)
Fig. 279. 22

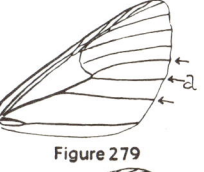

Figure 279

21b Vein running along lower side of discal cell
of front wing with four branches. (a)
Fig. 280. 23

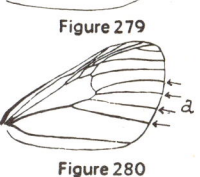

Figure 280

22a Hairy moths with heavy bodies; femora covered with long hairs.
(Prominents) Fig. 281.   Family 19, NOTODONTIDAE

Figure 281

Fig. 281. *Dàtana minìstra* Dru.
The Yellow-necked Caterpillar.

Front wings cinnamon brown,
marked with dark brown lines; hind
wings pale straw. Thorax with prominent red brown spot in front. The
larvae defoliate apple and other
trees. Expanse of wings 45-50 mm.
(U.S.D.A.)

Whether the Prominents are so called because of the hump on the
back of most of the larvae or from the lobe on the inner margin of the
front wing is uncertain. Either would do for a reason. These moths
are of medium size, but the family is a large one. The larvae feed on
the leaves of trees and shrubs.

22b Bodies slender; wings broad and delicate; legs not covered with long hairs. (Geometrids or Measuring Worms.) Fig. 282.
Family 26, GEOMETRIDAE

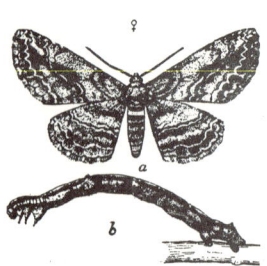

Figure 282

Fig. 282. *Cleòra pampinària* Guenee.
(a, Adult female; b, measuring worm larva.)

Tan with dark brown markings. Expanse of wings about 30 mm. (From U.S.D.A.)

The larvae of this family are the well known "measuring worms," which have but two pairs of prolegs instead of the customary five and in consequence walk with a looping movement. Many of these larvae when disturbed seek protection in holding themselves rigidly in a diagonal position from a limb, thus closely resembling a branched twig. Others drop from their feeding place and hang suspended on a few feet of silk. They climb back to their food when danger passes. The family includes many species.

23a Humeral veins in back wings, as pictured. Medium sized hairy moths with stout bodies; antennae pectinate. (Tent Caterpillars, Lackey Moths) Fig. 283.
Family 23, LASIOCAMPIDAE

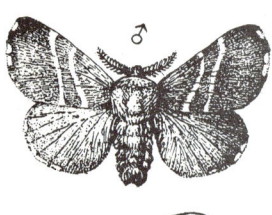

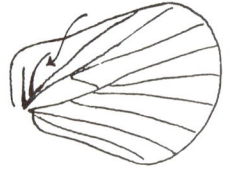

Figure 283

Fig. 283. *Malacosòma americànum* (F.)

Eastern Tent Caterpillar. (U.S.D.A.)

Light brown. The sexes are marked about the same, but the male moths are smaller and have more feathery antennae.

The family contains more than a thousand species and is found wherever forest or fruit trees grow. The caterpillars are gregarius and live in great numbers in thick webbed tents whenever the weather is unfavorable.

The Syrian Silk Worm, used in Europe in early times, belongs to this family.

23b Without humeral veins in back wings. 24

24a Stout, medium sized, hairy moths; the wings marked boldly in contrasting colors (a few forms plain white or yellow). Vein running along lower side of discal cell of hind wing, four-branched. (Tiger Moths, etc.) Fig. 284.

Family 14, ARCTIIDAE

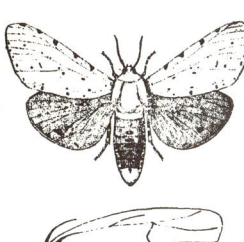

Figure 284

Fig. 284. *Estígmene acraèa* Dru.

The Salt-marsh Caterpillar.

Male (pictured) front wings, thorax, and tip of abdomen white; back wings and top of abdomen (except last segment) orange yellow. Spots on wings and mid-dorsal line of abdomen black. Female similar to male except that hind wings are white with black spots. This is one of our most common moths. Expanse of wings 50-60 mm. (From U.S.D.A.)

This is a large family. The caterpillars are for the most part heavily covered with hairs, which they weave into a loose cocoon when they pupate.

24b Front wings, at least, usually dull gray or brown. 25

25a Antennae usually thread-like, two ocelli often present; front margin of wings fairly straight. (A large percentage of moths flying into houses at night belong in this large family). (Owlet Moths) Fig. 285.

Family 16, NOCTUIDAE

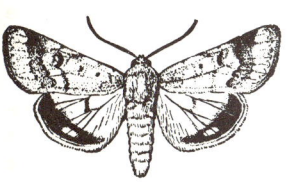

Figure 285

Fig. 285. *Helìothus armígera* (Hbn.)

The Corn Ear-worm.

Front wings straw colored, marked with brownish; hind wings creamy white marked with blackish. The larvae are altogether too common in the ears of sweet corn and not infrequently feed on field corn and tomatoes. Expanse of wing about 35-40 mm. (From U.S.D.A.)

The name Owlet Moths refers to the thick fluffy appearance of the members of this family and to the way their eyes shine at night. The family is one of the largest of the Lepidoptera, and highly variable. The "Underwings," fairly large moths with hind wings brilliantly striped with red and black or other outstanding color combinations belong here.

25b Antennae feathery, ocelli none; front margin of wings of male rounded; females wingless. (Tussock Moths.) Fig. 286.

Family 21, LYMANTRIIDAE

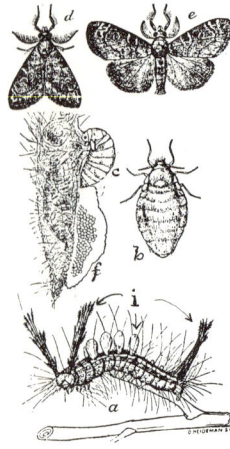

Figure 286

Fig. 286. *Hemerocámpa leuscostígma* A. & S.

The White Marked Tussock Moth. (a, Larva; b, female; c, female laying eggs on pupa case; d and e, adult males; f, egg mass.)

Female white, wingless. Male ashy gray with brown markings. The larvae are beautifully colored and marked with tufts and streamers of long scales (i). Expanse of wings about 35 mm. (From U.S.D.A.)

The greatly reduced wings of the female is characteristic of many members of this family. The larvae pupate on trees and buildings in late summer. The pupa case is often wrapped in a leaf. The adults emerge shortly and the female usually deposits her 250 to 700 eggs on the cocoon from which she emerged. The eggs are covered with a white weather proofing secretion. These egg masses may be easily seen and collected during the winter. The young caterpillars hatch when the trees begin to leaf out but will hatch somewhat earlier in a warm room. They will feed on a wide range of plants. It is an interesting project to rear a brood to the adult stage. There are two broods each year.

ORDER MECÓPTERA

1a With functional wings. 2

1b Wingless or with only vestigial wings. (Snow Scorpionflies). Fig. 287.

Family 2, BOREIDAE

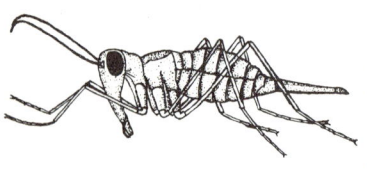

Figure 287

Fig. 287. *Bòreus califórnicus* Packard. Black. Common on snow along the Pacific coast in late winter. Length 3 mm.

There are only a few species of this family known. All are small and flightless but are good jumpers.

138

2a Tarsi with but one claw. Fig. 288.   **Family 3, BITTÁCIDAE**

Figure 288

Fig. 288. *Bíttacus apicàlis* Hagen.

Brownish. Spread of wings 30 mm.

The slender long-legged members of this rather small family strongly resemble crane flies. They have a peculiar way of hanging by their front feet and catching passing insects with their hind legs. A few species are wingless.

2b Two claws on each foot. (True Scorpionflies) Fig. 289.
Family 1, PANÓRPIDAE

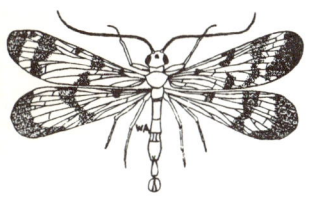

Figure 289

Fig. 289. *Panórpa venòsa* Westw.

Head light reddish brown; eyes, bodies and markings on wings dark brown. Length about 15 mm.

There are nearly fifty known species of this family in North America. Many of them have their wings beautifully mottled. They have an omnivorous diet dividing their tastes between plant foods and small insects, mites, etc.

ORDER DÍPTERA

1a Coxae close together, often touching. Abdominal segments showing. Wings usually present. 2

1b Wings absent or much reduced. (Some less common species winged but coxae always widely separated.) (Bird Parasite Flies.) Fig. 290.   **Family 81, HIPPOBÓSCIDAE**

Figure 290

Fig. 290. *Melóphagus ovinus* (L.)

The Sheep Tick.

Reddish brown, covered with long bristly hairs. Altogether too common on sheep and lambs. Length 5-6 mm.

The members of this small family are curious creatures, scarcely resembling flies. The larvae are full grown when born and immediately pupate. Some species are winged. One of these is rather common on owls and hawks.

2a Antennae with six or more free moving segments. (Usually 8 to 16). 3

2b Antennae with not more than five free moving segments; often with only three segments but the third frequently ringed or bearing a large bristle, or both. 11

3a Suture between the pro- and mesothorax V-shaped (a). Usually medium to large, loosely jointed, long-legged flies. (Crane Flies). Fig. 291.   **Family 4, TIPULIDAE**

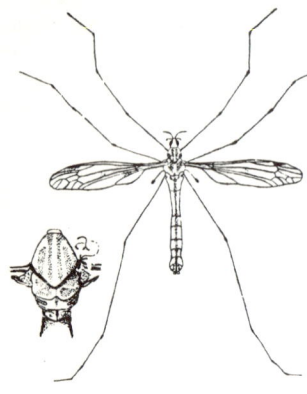

Figure 291

Fig. 291. *Tipula angustipénnis* Lw.

Head and thorax brownish gray; abdomen orange yellow with mid-dorsal stripe black. Wings smoky, with one dark brown and several whitish patches. Length 19-25 mm.

A large family of mosquito shaped flies. They are usually much larger than mosquitoes but some are very small. Their long legs are so fragile that it is a perplexing problem to mount and keep a collection of this family. They are most abundant in damp places. The larvae of some species are injurious to grass crops.

3b Thorax without V-shaped suture. 4

4a Veins and margins of wings fringed with scales. 5

4b Without scales as in 4a. 6

5a Wings long and comparatively narrow, with six nearly straight veins reaching the margin of the wing. (Mosquitoes) Fig. 292.   **Family 13, CULICIDAE**

Figure 292

Fig. 292. *Culex pipiens* L. The Northern House Mosquito.

Reddish brown; legs and bill blackish. Abdomen blackish above, with white bands at base of segments. Wing scales dark, hair-like. Length about 5 mm.

Everybody doubtless recognizes the mosquito at sight. Some species of mosquitoes do not bite and it is only the females of any species that bite. Some species serve as alternating host for several of man's worst diseases. This has given the mosquitoes a lot of publicity and made them notorious. They have been said to be man's worst enemies among the Diptera. Specimens should be handled with great care and mounted promptly. Even then it is difficult to keep them in good condition.

5b Wings broadly oval, often pointed at apex; held roof-like over body when at rest; thickly covered with hair-like scales. (Moth Flies) Fig. 293.　　　　　　　　Family 11, PSYCHÓDIDAE

Figure 293

Fig. 293. *Psychòda* sp.

Most of the moth flies are tiny little fellows which one may often see (if he looks closely) about the sink or other damp places. The larvae of some species live in drain pipes. Some species are blood suckers and may transmit diseases.

6a With ocelli but no discal cell in wing. 7

6b Without ocelli. 8

7a Antennae under the compound eyes, 8 to 12 segments; abdomen slender and somewhat flattened. (March Flies) Fig. 294.
　　　　　　　　　　　　　Family 17, BIBIÓNIDAE

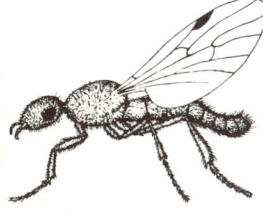

Figure 294

Fig. 294. *Bíbio* sp.

There are some 500 known species. Since the larvae feed in decaying organic matter the adults appear in great numbers when the conditions are right. They are for the most part medium sized, dark colored and usually hairy.

7b Antennae near middle of compound eye or higher; coxae usually much elongated (A); all tibiae with apical spurs (B); ocelli rarely absent. (Fungus Gnats) Fig. 295.
　　　　　　　　　　　　　Family 16, MYCETOPHÍLIDAE

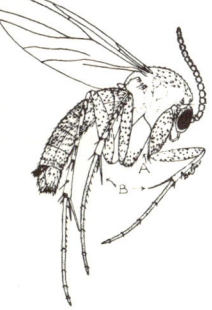

Figure 295

Fig. 295. *Leìa bivitátta* (Say)

This large family of some 2000 species is scattered the world over. They are rather small, somewhat mosquito-shaped flies. Many species feed in fungi and compete with other insects in hastily reducing these plants. The long coxa is a character for identification. The intensive study of one of these groups would make a fine avocation as well as a valuable contribution to science.

8a Costa (front marginal vein) continuing around the wing; wings usually with but three veins, small delicate flies with broad wings. (Gall Midges) Fig. 296.   Family 14, CECIDOMÝIDAE

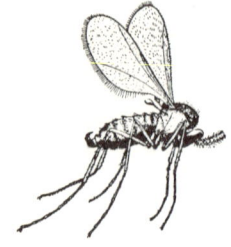

Figure 296

Fig. 296. *Dasyneùra rhodóphaga* Coq.

The Rose Midge.

Head and thorax brown; abdomen yellowish. Length 1-1¼ mm. (From U.S.D.A.)

The tiny members of this large family form galls or other deformities on many species of plants. The best way to collect them is to rear them from galls. The gall and a record of the plant on which it grew should always be preserved with the insect specimens. The Hessian fly, the Cloverleaf midge and the Wheat midge are among the well known pests belonging to this family.

8b Costa ending near tip of wing. 9

9a Wings broad, their front veins heavy, the others weak; antennae shorter than the thorax. (Black Flies) Fig. 297.
Family 7, SIMULIIDAE

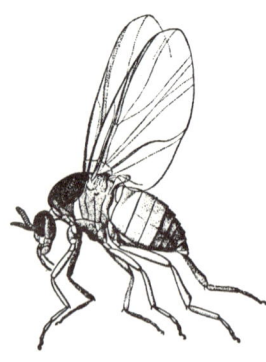

Figure 297

Fig. 297. *Prosimùlium pecuàrum* (Riley)

The Buffalo-gnat.

Black, the base of the abdomen lighter. One of the larger members of the family. Length about 4 mm. (From U.S.D.A.)

The members of this family are exceedingly annoying to man and his domestic animals. The gnats are small, humpbacked and most persistent food-getters. Their bites are annoying at the time but with many species become more irritating somewhat later. They make an interesting addition to the collection but are otherwise good insects to keep away from.

9b Wings long and narrow, their back veins well developed.......10

10a Wings held roof-like over the back when at rest; legs long and slender; antennae of males plume-like. (Midges, Gnats) Fig. 298. Family 9, CHIRONÓMIDAE

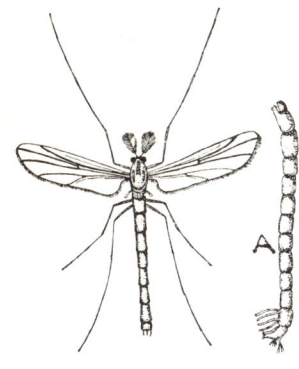

Figure 298

Fig. 298. *Chirónomus lineátus* Say

Thorax very light greenish gray with mid-dorsal stripe of dark brown and lateral markings of light brown. Abdomen pale green with lateral lines of pale brown. Eyes dark reddish brown. Length about 10 mm.

Most of the Midges are unable to bite although they look much like mosquitoes. The air is often filled with the adults and at night they become so numerous about our lights as to drive us from our work. Our water courses are filled with their larvae (A), which doubtless plays a very important part in feeding young fish.

10b Wings held flat over the back when at rest; tiny slender flies with long antennae and vicious biting mouth parts. (Biting Gnats, Punkies) Fig. 299. Family 10, CERATOPOGÓNIDAE

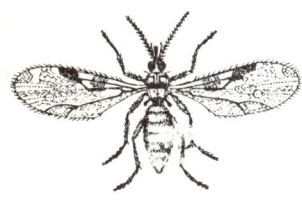

Figure 299

Fig. 299. *Culicòides* sp.

These pests are most abundant near water courses especially the seashore. The adults of some species attack insects instead of mammals. The term "no-see-ems" derives from the fact that they are so small. The larvae develops in water, mud and decaying vegetation.

11a Antennae of 4 segments, the 4th elongated and often thickened; but one ocellus; only one or two veins reach the wing margin back of the apex. Often very large. (Mydas Flies) Fig. 300. Family 26, MYDAIDAE

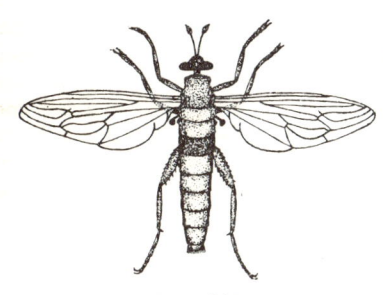

Figure 300

Fig. 300. *Mỳdas clavàtus* Fabr.

Velvety black with orange band at base of abdomen; wings brown with darker veins.

The family is small but some very large flies belong to it, some reaching a length of 2 inches and a wing expanse of more than 3 inches. Both the adults and larvae are predaceous.

143

11b **Antennae with three segments, the third often with a more or less branching bristle (arista). Fig. 301.** 12

12a **Third segment of antennae with rings, often long and seeming to consist of several segments. (Fig. 301A)** 13

12b **Third segment of antennae not ringed, but bearing an elongate style or arista. (Fig. 301B)** 14

Figure 301

13a **Discal cell (a) small, its dimensions usually nearly equal; squamae small or vestigial; no spurs on tibiae. (Soldier Flies.) Fig. 302.**
Family 20, **STRATIOMYIDAE**

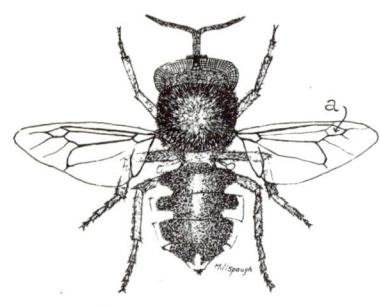

Figure 302

Fig. 302. *Stratiomyia meiginii* Wied.

Bluish black; thorax covered at sides with gray pubescence. Margins of abdomen marked with yellow which turns in towards center at back of each segment. Tip of abdomen with mid-dorsal yellow line. Length 12-14 mm.

The Soldier Flies apparently get the name from the bright colored stripes with which many species are decorated. The members range in size from small to fairly large and vary a great deal in shape. Many species are found on flowers.

13b **Discal cell at least twice as long as wide (a); squamae large; two spurs at tip of middle tibiae. (Horse Flies) Fig. 303.**
Family 22, **TABANIDAE**

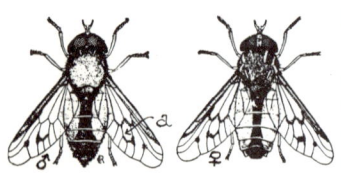

Figure 303

Fig. 303. *Tabànus lasiophthálmus* Macq.

Thorax black with narrow gray stripes; wings hyaline; markings on wings brown. Abdomen broadly reddish on sides. Eyes pilose. Length 13-15 mm. (From U.S.D.A.)

These merciless pests of man and beast range from medium to large size. The males do not suck blood but feed on the nectar or pollen of flowers. *Tularaemia* and other serious diseases are known to be transmitted by Horse Flies. It is a large family.

14a Small to very small "hunch-backed" flies; head small; wings with two strong longitudinal veins and 4 or 5 fine ones; often wingless. (Hump-backed Flies) Fig. 304.

Family 36, PHÓRIDAE

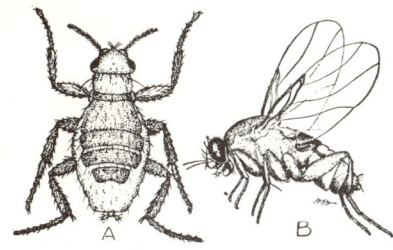

Figure 304

Fig. 304. A, *Pulicóphora* sp., A wingless Phorid; B, *Aphiochaeta perdita*, a parasite of the alfalfa caterpillar. (U.S.-D.A.)

The antennae and wing venation when present are characteristic of the family. The wingless members walk with a peculiar jerky movement. Many species inhabit the nests of ants.

14b Not as in 14a. 15

15a Vein above anterior cross vein two-branched (Radius four-branched. See Figs. 306 and 310. 16

15b Vein above anterior cross vein unbranched (Radius three-branched). See Fig. 312. 20

16a Top of head hollowed between the eyes. Fig. 305. 17

16b Top of head not hollowed. 18

Figure 305

17a Head strongly concave when viewed from in front (A), three ocelli, medium to large, bristly flies. (Assassin Flies) Fig. 306.

Family 27, ASÍLIDAE

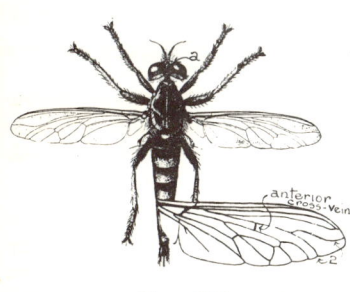

Figure 306

Fig. 306. *Prómachus vertebrátus* Say

Thorax black, more or less thickly covered with gray pubescence. Abdomen pale gray with black cross bar at base of each segment. Tibiae and tarsi orange yellow, sometimes marked with blackish. Covered pretty much throughout with long gray hairs. Length 28-35 mm. (From U.S.-D. A.)

True to their name these highwaymen of the insect world wait in some advantageous post along the paths frequented by insects, and many an unfortunate insect suffers from their attacks. There are many known species, some of which are quite large. Gray is the predominating color. Their choice of habitat is much varied in different species. The collector who wishes to get the largest number of species will visit a wide variety of regions.

17b Top of head convex (but below the level of the eyes); eyes of males grown together or very narrowly separated. (Snipe Flies) Fig. 307.   Family 24, RHAGIÓNIDAE

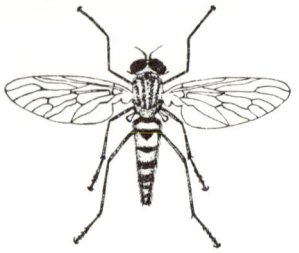

Figure 307

Fig. 307. *Rhàgio mystàcea* Macq.

These flies have long legs. They are small to medium sized and live a predaceous life both as adults and larvae. They are common on the foliage in wooded areas. Some blood sucking species attack man.

18a Wing with but 4 or less posterior cells. Fig. 308A. 19

18b Wing with 5 posterior cells (Fig. 308B); eyes of males usually united or nearly so; antennae usually with a sharp terminal style on third segment. (Stilleto Flies) Fig. 309.
**   Family 28, THERÉVIDAE**

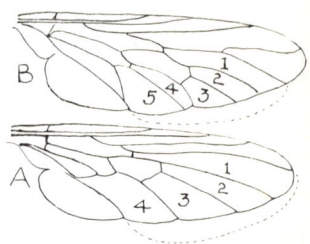

Figure 308

Fig. 309. *Pherócera signítifrons*

This is a comparitively small family of medium sized flies, which rather closely resemble the Assilids. The wings are unmistakably characteristics. They seem to prefer dry areas and are fairly abundant.

Figure 309

The members of this family average somewhat smaller and are likely not so well known as the Assasin Flies. These, too, live on the blood of other insects for which they station themselves and capture on the wing as the innocent victim goes about his business. Their colors are often gray and black, though occasional species are more brightly marked.

The long cylindrical larvae live in the soil and in decaying vegetation and are predacious. Less than 400 species have been described.

19a Anal cell open (a), or closed near the wing margin, the anal vein always reaching the margin. (Bee Flies) Fig. 310.

Family 30, BOMBYLIIDAE

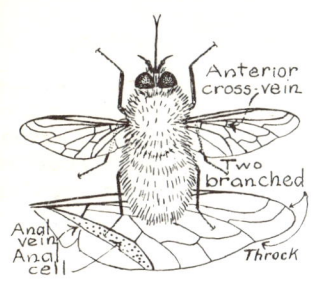

Figure 310

Fig. 310. *Sparnopòlius fúlvus* Wied.

Black, thickly covered with golden yellow hairs. Frequent, hovering over flowers or alighting on them. Length 9-10 mm.

There is considerable variation in size and shape of the bee flies. Many of them look like fluffy little balls lazily dangling over a flower, where they feed on pollen and nectar. The larvae are parasitic on other insects. Since the hairs, which rub off easily, are necessary for identification the collector must be very careful with specimens of this family.

19b Anal cell closed, remote from wing margin (a); anal vein never reaching margin, sometimes wanting. (Dance Flies) (in part) Fig. 311.

Family 33, EMPIDAE

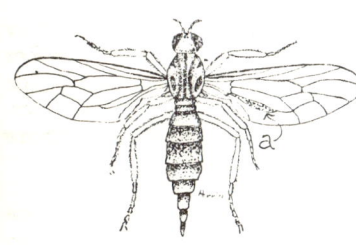

Figure 311

Fig. 311. *Rhamphomyia rava* Lw.

Head, thorax and abdomen feebly marked with brown. Eyes dark reddish brown. Wings and legs yellowish brown. Length about 9 mm.

Who has not watched with wonder the swarms of small to medium sized flies, often seen floating with up and down movements in the shade of a tree? They are predacious, luckily, — the world would soon be overrun with insects if many of them were not set against the others. The family is a large one.

Much has been written about the mating habits of this family. In many instances the male brings an offering of food and it seems in some cases that mating cannot proceed except as the female feeds on this provided prey. With other species the male blows a big bubble or resorts to some other "monkey-shine" much as many male birds and mammals employ to get the attention of their mate.

20a A spurious (extra) vein running diagonally between the third and fourth veins (a), bisecting the anterior cross vein; anal cell closed near wing margin. (Flower Flies.) Fig. 312.

Family 39. SÝRPHIDAE

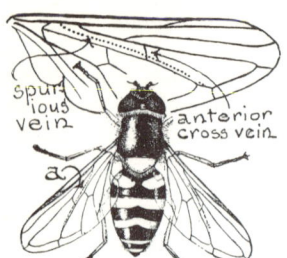

Fig. 312. *Sýrphus ribèsii* L.

Blackish with pale yellow markings. Its larvae feed on the melon aphid. Length 7-8 mm. (From U.S.D.A.)

Figure 312

The flower flies are doubly valuable. Many of them feed in their larval state on plant lice and mealy bugs. Nearly all of them make a valuable contribution in pollinating plants. They look like bees and often act like them, which doubtless gives them much protection from the birds and other enemies. This is one of the largest families of Diptera.

20b No spurious vein. **21**

21a Anal cell (See Fig. 318) long, rarely incomplete; head large, spherical, broader than thorax. (Big-headed Flies) Fig. 313.

Family 38. PIPUNCULIDAE

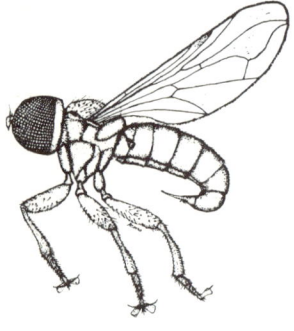

Fig. 313. *Dorilas àter* (Meig)

The big eyes covering practically all of the head make these flies rather easy to distinguish. Their eggs are laid on *Hemiptera* and *Homoptera* within which the larvae feed as parasites. The leafhoppers and the plant bugs suffer most in this way.

Figure 313

21b Anal cell short or wanting. (See Fig. 318) **22**

22a Frontal lunule (a crescent shaped sclerite just above antennae) present. Fig. 314. .... **24**
Fig. 314. Diagrammatic front view of head.

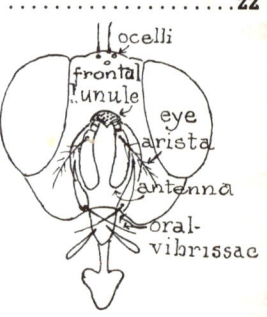

22b Frontal lunule wholly absent. **23**

Figure 314

23a Second basal cell (A) always united with discal cell to form one cell; anterior cross vein small and not more than one-fourth the length of wing from its base; small, usually metallic green or blue flies. (Long-Legged Flies.) Fig. 315.   Family 34, DOLICHOPIDAE

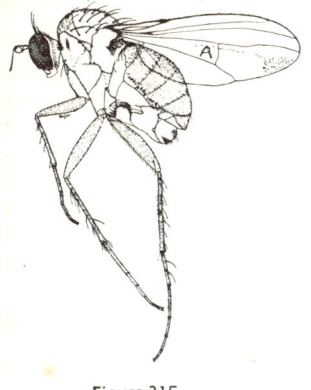

Figure 315

Fig. 315. *Dolichopus jàquesi* H. & K.

Bright metallic green; legs, eyes and spots at tip of wings blackish. Length 5-6 mm.

These flies are small, almost always under ten millimeters in length. Most of them are metallic green or blue, and have longer legs than the other related families. They feed on smaller insects and mites. They are found in a rather wide range of habitats and are represented by many species. This would seem to be a good family for some enthusiastic amateur collector.*

23b Anterior cross vein well beyond the basal fourth of the wing, or the second basal cell complete; anal vein never reaching the margin, sometimes wanting. (Dance Flies) (in part) See Fig. 311.
Family 33, EMPIDAE

The slender cylindrical larvae of the Dance Flies are found in the soil, vegetable debris, mosses and in other damp places. They are predacious. The family numbers close to 2000 known species.

24a Squamae (scale-like lobe—usually whitish—below base of wing) large. Fig. 316. 37

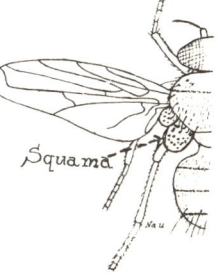

Figure 316

24b Squamae small or absent. 25

Since first writing this sentence some years ago, Bernard Berger as one of our students, added more than 100 species from this family to those already known for the State of Iowa. Quoting Admiral Dewey "What man has done, man can do."

25a Mouthparts vestigial; hidden in a small oval opening.
(Horse Bot Fly.) Fig. 317.   Family 75, GASTROPHILIDAE

Figure 317

Fig. 317. *Gasteróphilus intestinàlis* De G.

The Horse Bot Fly.

Yellowish brown, thickly covered with hairs, somewhat resembling a honey bee. Wings are mottled and abdomen ringed with brown. Lays its eggs on legs of horses. Length 12-14 mm.

There are but three species of this family known in the United States. The larvae attach themselves to the wall of the stomach, throat, nasal passages and intestines of horses and if present in large numbers greatly reduce the horses' efficiency.

25b Oral opening large; mouthparts well developed. 26

26a Anal cell (between 5th and 6th veins)
present. Fig. 318. 29
Fig. 318. Wing of 'Trupaneid showing anal cell.

Figure 318

26b Anal cell absent. 27

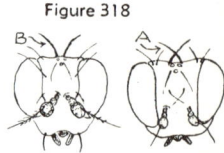

Figure 319

27a Post-ocellar bristles (on top of head just
back of the ocelli) turning toward each
other or absent. Fig. 319A. 28

27b Post-ocellar bristles diverging (Fig. 319B); face usually much
rounded. Small to very small flies living in damp places. (Shore
Flies) Fig. 320.   Family 61, EPHYDRIDAE

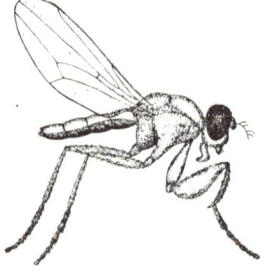

Figure 320

Fig. 320. *Ochthèra humilis*

These flies belong in the marshes and other wet places, and are often found along the seashore. Some can walk on the surface film of water. The larvae seem to be largely vegetable feeders, some living in decaying vegetation; others within living plants.

A few adults possess pictured wings.

28a **Vein under discal cell without a sharp curve; triangle bearing the ocelli small (A); antennae usually pulmose (C). (Vinegar Flies). Fig. 321.** **Family 55, DROSOPHILIDAE**

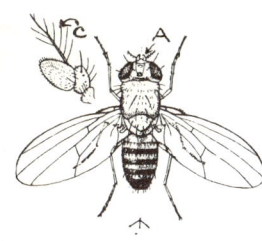

Figure 321

Fig. 321. *Drosóphila melanogáster* Meig.

(a, Adult; b, antenna.)

Grayish brown with dark markings on thorax and tip of abdomen. Eyes bright red. This is the little fly so common at fruit stands. It is now used extensively in studying genetics. Length about 3 mm. (From U.S.D.A.)

The members of this family are usually under 5 mm. in length. They are found wherever overripe fruit or vegetables abound. Some feed on sap and fungi.

Their life cycle is short and their multiplication rapid.

28b **Vein under discal cell with a sharp curve (A); triangle bearing the ocelli large. Usually naked flies. (Frit Flies) Fig. 322.** **Family 60, CHLORÓPIDAE**

Figure 322

Fig. 322. *Myromўza americàna* Fitch
The Wheat-stem Maggot.

Yellowish-white marked with black on thorax and abdomen as pictured. Eyes bright green. Length 5-6 mm.

The Frit Flies are very small, smooth flies. Many of them attack the stems of grasses where the larvae develop. Our cereal plants have several rather serious pests in this family.

29a **Wings pictured (with darkened or colored design). Fig. 323.** 33

29b **Wings usually not pictured; usually small flies.** 30

Figure 323

30a **Front vein (costa) broken at first (humeral) cross vein.** 31

30b **Costa not as in 30a.** 34

31a Post-ocellar bristles if present diverging (See Fig. 319B); if wanting the antennae bear no arista. (Leaf-mining Flies) Fig. 324.
Family 58, AGROMYZIDAE

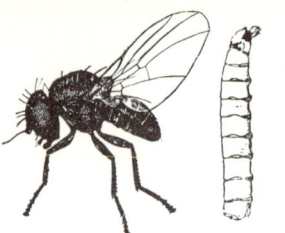

Figure 324

Fig. 324. *Melanagromyza simplex* (Loew.)
The Asparagus Miner. 3-4 mm. (U.S.D.A.)

This fairly large family live for the most
part as miners in leaves and stems of
plants. The species pictured here "mines"
under the surface of young asparagus
stems making them less marketable.

31b With an arista; post-ocullar bristles if present not diverging.....32
32a Anterior frontal bristles (above base of antennae) converging.
Fig. 325. Family 59, PHYLLOMYZIDAE

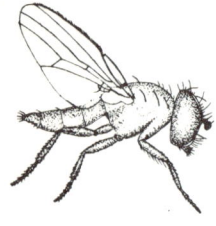

Figure 325

Fig. 325. *Milichia leucogáster*.

These small, often black flies are largely
miners as larvae. The adults are lovers of
sunny places and may be found thus exposing
themselves.

Much work needs to be done with several
families of these smaller flies. They offer excellent possibilities for the careful student.

32b Frontal bristles (above base of antennae) not converging; arista
usually long and pulmose. (Vinegar Flies) (in part) (See Fig. 321)
Family 55, DROSOPHILIDAE

33a Vibrissae (large bristles, one on either side of oral opening) present (see Fig. 314), though sometimes indistinct. Legs moderate
length. Abdomen with 4-5 segments. (Fruit Flies.) Fig. 326.
Family 43, TRUPANEIDAE

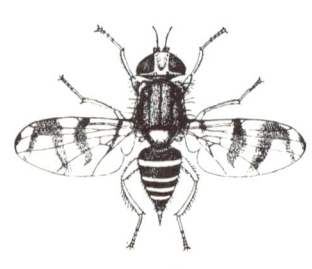

Figure 326

Fig. 326. *Rhagóletis cingulàta* (Lw.)
The Cherry Fruit Fly. (U.S.D.A.)

Blackish. Thorax with yellow margins, abdomen with white bands. Length
about 5 mm.

The adults of this family are frequently found on flowers. The larvae live in
fruit, and seeds. Some are leaf miners.
Others make galls. The round knobs
so frequently seen on the stems of gold-
en rod are made by one of these flies.
Many of these flies have very peculiar
faces when viewed in profile.

33b Vibrissae absent (see Fig. 314). Legs short, abdomen with 5 or 6 segments. (Pictured-Wing Flies.) Fig. 327.

Family 42, OTITIDAE

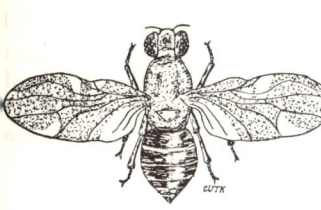

Fig. 327. *Delphínia picta.* Fab.

Head, thorax and abdomen reddish brown. Eyes darker, scutellum yellowish brown. Wings opaque, in reddish brown and white. Length 7-8 mm.

In size these Pictured wing flies range from small to moderately large. They are most common in damp places.

Figure 327

34a Body cylindrical; head spherical; small shining reddish or black flies. Found around excrement, carrion, etc. (Spiny-legged Flies) Fig. 328. Family 52, SEPSIDAE

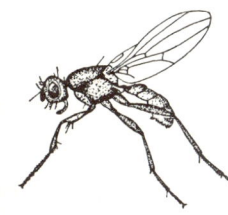

Fig. 328. *Meroplius sterorarius* Desv.

Black, shining. 3 mm.

The larvae of this rather small family feed in carrion, excrement and decaying vegetation. The adults are found around these food sources also. The anal cell is very short.

Figure 328

34b Not as in 34a. 35

35a Frontal plates (on sides of front below eyes) (A) wide; oral vibrissae present (see Fig. 314); apical cell widely open. (Sun Flies) Fig. 329. Family 72, HELOMYZIDAE

Fig. 329. *Pseudoleria pectinata* Loew.

This is a fairly sizeable family of medium sized "funny-faced" flies. The larvae are scavengers so the adults may be found around plant and animal wastes.

Curran recommends burying a tin can with its open end flush with the ground and examining in early morning for adults.

Figure 329

35b Frontal plates narrow; oral vibrissae absent. 36

36a Usually small flies; apical cell (A) widely open at wing margin (a few exceptions in species with short, wide abdomen) Fig. 330.
Family 53, LAUXANIIDAE

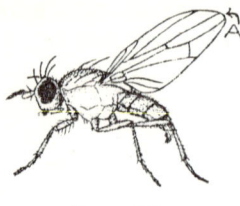

Figure 330

Fig. 330. *Minéttia* sp.

Only a few American genera have been named for this family of medium to small flies. They occur most abundantly in moist places and are very active at the close of day. Some larvae live in decaying vegetation while others are plant miners.

36b Medium sized flies with broad head; apical cell (A) closed or much narrowed. (Thick-headed Flies) Fig. 331. Family 40, CONOPIDAE

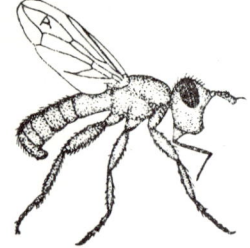

Figure 331

Fig. 331. *Myòpa claúsa* Lw.

These flies have a broad head often with concave face. They are medium sized and some species are rapid flyers for they often lay their eggs on their Hymenopterous hosts while in flight. They are rather common on flowers and in this situation seem rather sluggish.

37a Metascutellum developed, appearing as a strong convexity below the scutellum (a), hypopleura (h) with strong bristles. (Tachinids.) Figs. 332 and 333.
Family 79, TACHINIDAE *

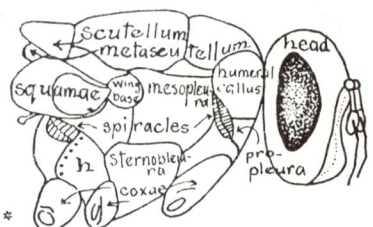

Figure 332

Fig. 333. *Phorócera claripénnis* Macq.

Black, with metallic bluish sheen. Head and thorax with gray hairs. Scutellum brown. Squamae whitish, prominent. Length about 8 mm. (From U.S.D.A.)

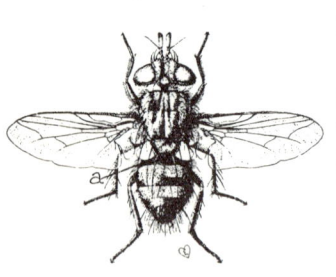

Figure 333

This is one of our most helpful families of flies. The family is a large one. Its members are parasitic on other insects, many of them destroying caterpillars. It is a very common sight to find the adults busily flying through low plants searching for victims on which to deposit an egg.

* This family is now known by some specialists as **Larvaevoridae.**

154

37b Metascutellum weak or absent, or if developed there is only hair (no bristles) on the hypopleura. **38**

38a Oral opening and mouthparts very small; scutellum very short. (Bot Flies.) Fig. 334. Family 78, OESTRIDAE

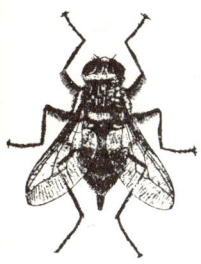

Figure 334

Fig. 334. *Hypodérma lineátum* (De Vill.)

The Common Cattle Grub.

Hairy. Black with bands and markings of pale yellow. Larvae mature under skin of cattle. Length 12-14 mm. (From U.S.D.A.)

The family contains only a very few species, all of which are parasitic in the larval stage on mammals.

38b Oral opening and mouthparts of normal size. **39**

39a Hypoleura with a row of bristles. **40**

39b Hypoleura with fine short hairs or bare; oral vibrissae present. Fig. 335. Family 74, MUSCIDAE

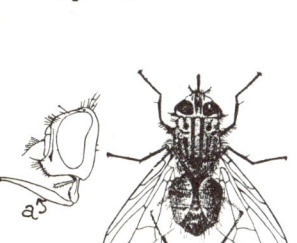

Figure 335

Fig. 335. *Stomóxys calcitrans* L.

The Stable Fly.

Black and gray. Rather closely resembles the house fly. Common about stables and domestic animals. Bites viciously (a). Length 6-7 mm. (From U.S.D.A.)

The family Muscidae as here defined by the key is as set forth by Curran in his recent "North American Diptera," and would include many species placed with other families by earlier writers. The group includes many serious pests of plants as well as of animals.

40a Apical (first posterior) cell strongly narrowed or closed at wing margin (A). (Flesh Flies.) Fig. 336. Family 76, METOPIIDAE

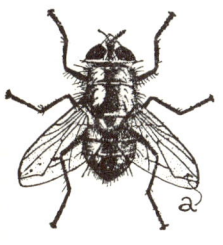

Figure 336

Fig. 336. *Lucília caèsar* L. The Green Bottle Fly.

Abdomen bright metallic blue or oftener green. Common around garbage and carrion. Length about 8 mm. (From U.S.D.A.)

The members of this family are moderately small to medium sized flies. Many are mottled gray and black. Others have their abdomens metallic green or blue. The larvae are largely scavengers, and flesh feeders. Some are parasitic.

40b Apical cell not at all narrowed at wing margin (c). Fig. 337.
Family 74, MUSCIDAE

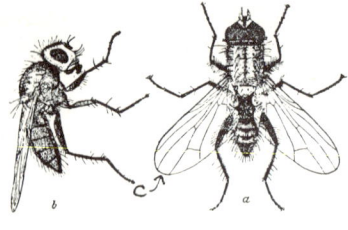

Figure 337

Fig. 337. *Hylemya brássicae* (Bouche)

The Cabbage Maggot. (a, Dorsal view; b, side view.)

Black and gray. The maggots live in the roots of cabbage and related plants producing decay. Length 5 6 mm. (From U.S.D.A.)

ORDER SIPHONÁPTERA

1a Thorax not greatly shortened, the three dorsal segments together being at least longer than the first abdominal segment. 2

1b Thorax much shortened, its three segments together not equalling the first abdominal segment. (The Sticktight Fleas.) Fig. 338.
Family 6, HECTOPSYLLIDAE

Fig. 338. *Echidnóphaga gallinácea* (Westw.)

The Sticktight Flea. (U.S.D.A.)

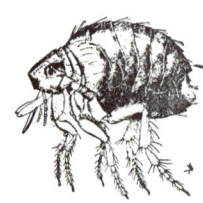

Figure 338

Attaches itself around head and other soft parts of poultry and some native birds. It ranges through the South and is highly destructive.

This family differs from other families of fleas by the individuals remaining fixed to one place on their host. The abdomen of the female becomes greatly distended with eggs. The Chigoe or Jigger Flea of the tropics also belongs here. It infests man and other animals but should not be confused with our common "chigger" which is a mite.

2a Suture connecting bases of the antennae separating front of head from hinder part as pictured. Fig. 339.
Family 3, HYSTRICHOPSYLLIDAE

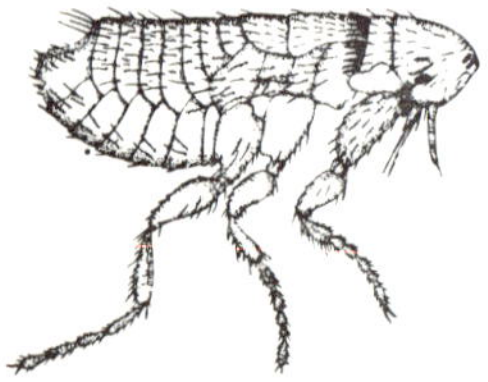

Fig. 339. *Ctenopsýllus segnis* (Schoen.)

Found on mice and rats the world over.

This family gives its attention to rodents. The fleas have their spines arranged in characteristic way which offers a useful character for identification.

Figure 339

2b Without the suture described in 1a. **3**

3a Back with but one row of bristles on each segment; eyes present. Fig. 340. Family 1, PULÍCIDAE

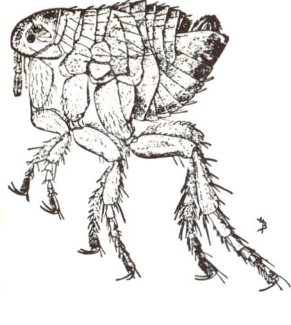

Figure 340

Fig. 340. *Pùlex írritans* L. The Human Flea. Reddish brown. Length 2-3 mm. (U.S.-D.A.)

In our country the dog and cat flea are more abundant and are frequently the species attacking man. They belong to this same family, as do many other species attacking practically all mammals.

In their immature stages these fleas are very slender whitish worms which live in nest of their host, cracks in the floor, etc. It's a lot easier to get fleas in a house than it is to get them out, as many of your friends can tell you.

3b Often without eyes; back with two or more rows of bristles on each segment. Fig. 341. Family 2, DOLICHOPSÝLLIDAE

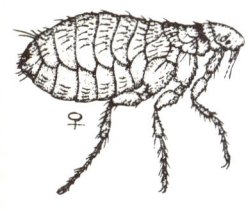

Figure 341

Fig. 341. *Nosopsyllus fasciàtus* (Bosc.)

The Common Rat Flea. Found on rats both in America and Europe. It transmits bubonic plague.

The family is the largest one of the order and is a highly important one. About 30 genera have been described.

ORDER HYMENÓPTERA

1a Base of abdomen broadly joined to the thorax; always two segments of trochanter. **2**

1b Abdomen joined to thorax by a slender petiole of varying length..5

2a Fore leg with but one terminal spur on tibia. Fig. 342A. **3**

2b Fore leg with two terminal spurs on tibia. Fig. 342B. **4**

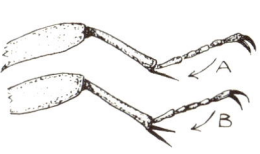

Figure 342

157

3a **Ovipositor rigidly exserted, nearly half as long as abdomen; back margin of pronotum curving inward; antennae not clubbed; wood borers. (Horn Tails.) Fig. 343.** Family 5, SIRICIDAE

Fig. 343. *Trémex colúmba* L.

The Pigeon Tremex.

Brownish yellow, marked with dark brown. Wings brownish yellow with light brown veins. Figure is of female. Male has abdomen wholly brown and lacks ovipositon The eggs are laid in the trunks of oak, apple, elm and other trees where the larvae bore. Length 20-45 mm.

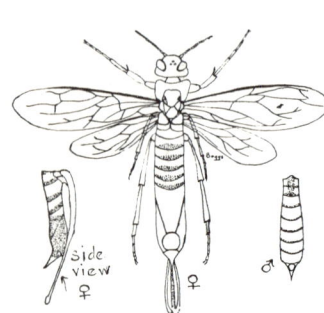

Figure 343

This family is a small one. The members are elongate with subcylindrical bodies. The females bore holes in the trunks of trees with the stiff ovipositor and lay one egg in a place. The larvae develops as wood borers.

This very showy Pigeon Tremex is parasitized by an equally showy Ichneumon Wasp (see Fig. 359) which employs its 3 or 4 inch long ovipositors to penetrate the wood and insert its egg within the tunnel where the Tremex grub is living.

3b **Ovipositor barely evident; antennae clubbed. (Stem-Sawflies.) Fig. 344.** Family 3, CEPHIDAE

Fig. 344. *Cèphus cínctus* Norton

The Wheat Stem Sawfly.

Black, shining; abdomen prominently marked with three yellow crossbands; wings smoky; legs yellow. A pest of wheat and other small grains. Length 6-8 mm.

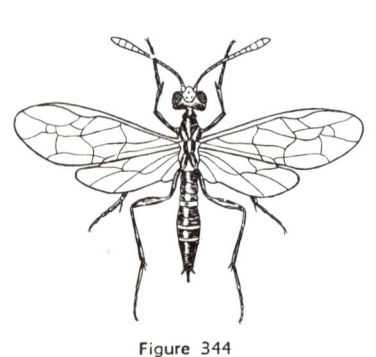

Figure 344

The members of this family bore into the stems of grasses and other herbaceous plants and into the young shoots of trees and shrubs. They are insects of moderate size, rather slender and elongate.

4a Antennae clubbed; large insects. **Fig. 345.**

Family 6, CRABRONIDAE

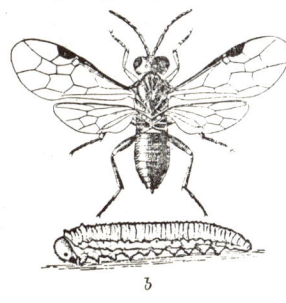

Figure 345

Fig. 345. *Cimbex americàna* (Leach)
The Elm Sawfly.

Head, thorax and base of abdomen black except for a bright yellow spot. Remainder of abdomen brownish red. Antennae yellowish brown. Wings smoky. The larvae feed on the leaves of willow and elm. Length 20-28 mm. (From U.S.D.A.)

The family is not large. The larvae are grub-like but bear eight pairs of prolegs which distinguish them from either the caterpillars or beetle larvae.

4b Antennae not clubbed. Medium sized species. **(The Typical Saw-flies) Fig. 346.**

Family 9, TENTHREDINIDAE

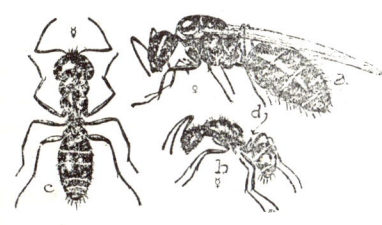

b

Figure 346

Fig. 346. *Endelòmyia aèthiops* (F.)
Rose Slug. A, adult; b, slug.

Head, body, legs and antennae black. Wings smoky with brown veins. The larvae are green slugs which feed upon the upper surface of the leaves of roses. Length of adults about 5 mm. (From U.S.D.A.)

Sawflies are abundant both in individuals and species. Many of them are marked with sharply contrasting colors. The imported currant worms, abundant in spring on currants and gooseberries, and the pear slugs are common examples of the larvae of the family. The latter like many other species are shiny.

5a Slender petiole of abdomen bearing a node or erect scale (d). Usually wingless. Males and queens winged at mating season. **(Ants.) Fig. 347.**

Family 52, FORMICIDAE

Fig. 347. *Camponòtus herculeànus pennsylvánicus* De G.
The Black Carpenter Ant. (a, Winged queen; b, worker minor; c, worker major.)

Black or dark brown. Our largest ant. Lives in logs, eating galleries in the wood. Sometimes destructive to buildings. Length 7-16 mm. (From U.S.D.A.)

Figure 347

Ants may be found almost everywhere. They live a highly successful community life, build houses, harvest crops, keep their domestic animals and pets, and do many other highly interesting things.

5b Petiole not as in 5a. **6**

6a Wingless (females) or winged (males); thorax or wide band on abdomen thickly covered with red hairs; hind tarsus slender and
cylindrical. (Velvet Ants.) Fig. 348.   Family 50, MUTILLIDAE

Figure 348

Fig. 348. *Dasymutilla occidentàlis* (L.)
The Cow-killer Ant.

Brick red and black as pictured; covered with
thick plush-like hairs. Length 16-30 mm. The
males are similarly colored but have wings.

These insects run actively in sandy areas.
Some species are covered with long hairs. The
females seem innocent but sting viciously if
picked up. There are some 3000 known species.

6b Winged; without covering of reddish hair.
(or if with red hairs, tarsi broad and
flat.) **7**

Figure 349

7a Hind leg with two trochanters, i. e. three
small segments between femur and thor-
ax. Fig. 349A. **8**

7b Hind leg with but one trochanter, i. e. two small segments between
femur and thorax. Fig. 349B. **17**

8a Front wings without closed cells. Mostly very small parasitic
wasps. **9**

8b Front wings with one or more closed cells. **14**

9a Hind wings linear with still more slender stem-like base. Very small
egg parasites. (Fairy Flies) Fig. 350.

Family 40, MYMÁRIDAE

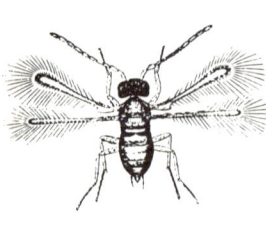

Figure 350

Fig. 350. *Metaláptus torgùatus* Mel.

Black and yellow. Less than one-third
milimeter in length. (After Melanotti).

This family of some 200 described species contains some of our smallest insects.
They are parasitic in the eggs of other
insects. One would need to live in another world of tiny things to appreciate such
little fellows as these. When we realize
that they probably have as many muscles
as we have we get some new notions of
the perfection of Nature.

9b Hind wings not as in 9a. **10**

10a Tarsi with 4 or 5 segments. **11**

10b Tarsi with 3 segments; antennae with 3 to 8 segments. (Trichogrammatid Egg Parasites) Fig. 351.

Family 39, TRICHOGRAMMÁTIDAE

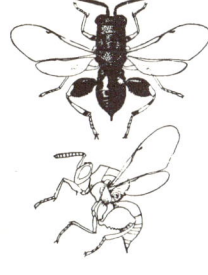

Fig. 351. *Trichogramma minùtum* Rly. Microscopic (U.S.D.A.)

This tiny little lady patiently bores a hole into the egg of another insect, there to leave her own egg and thus doom its host to misery before it is hatched. The importance of egg parasites can scarcely be over estimated. They are sometimes reared to be liberated where badly needed.

Figure 351

11a Hind femora ot normal size; thorax not greatly enlarged. 12

11b Hind femora greatly enlarged; thorax large. (Chalcid Flies) Fig. 352.

Family 31, CHALCÍDIDAE

Fig. 352. *Brachyméria ovàta* (Say)

Hind femora black, with white or yellow spot at tip. Head and thorax heavily punctured but dorsal surface of abdomen without punctures. Tegulae wholly white or yellow. Length 3.5-7 mm. (From U.S.D.A.)

In this family belong some of the tiniest of all insects, some being only one-fourth of a millimeter in length. Black is the predominating color; many have a metallic sheen. The head is proportionately large and the wings with but few veins. Some very important egg parasites belong here. Some species infest seeds and are harmful.

Figure 352

12a Hind tibia (A) with one spur at end; antennae elbowed with long basal joint. Usually with metallic sheen. 13

12b Hind tibiae with two spurs at end (A); pronotum wide and somewhat square. Black or yellow. (Straw Worms, Joint Worms) Fig. 353.

Family 32, EURYTÓMIDAE

Fig. 353. *Harmolìta gràndis* (Riley) The Wheat Strawworm.

There are both winged and wingless forms. The larva in the stems of wheat makes a gall and weakens the plant. (U.S.D.A.)

This large family contains many parasitic species but there are others like the one pictured here which are plant feeders. They are usually black or metallic.

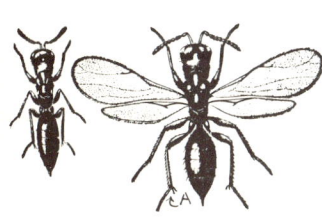

Figure 353

161

13a Antennae with but 4-8 segments. (Sun Flies, Scale Parasites)
Fig. 354. **Family 37, APHELINIDAE**

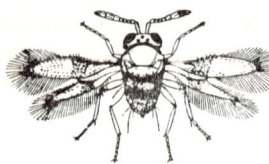

Figure 354

Fig. 354. *Aspidiotiphagus citrinus* How.
A parasite of the San Jose Scale. (U.S.-D.A.)

This is a large and widely scattered family of parasites of aphids, scale insects and whiteflies, their larva spending its life span within one of these tiny hosts. The adults feed on honey dew. They are often brilliantly marked and display much metallis coloration. Such miniature life seems to open up another world, and would make the stories of fairyland seem plausible.

13b Antennae with 13 segments. (Jewel Wasps) Fig. 355.
Family 36, PTEROMALIDAE

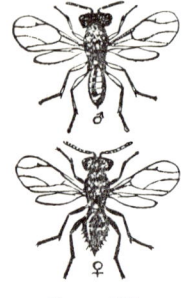

Figure 355

Fig. 355. *Pteromalus puparum* (L.)
A common parasite of the imported cabbage-worm. (U.S.D.A.)

This is another large cosmopolitan family. Metallic greens, blues, golds, coppers, etc., with many iridescent sheens make a pagent fit for any stage. The difficulty, — these gaily decorated actors are only 1-2 mm. long. Then they have some very important things to do for they must find all the caterpillars and other insects they parasite in order to lay their eggs at just the proper time.

14a Front wings without a dark thickened spot (stigma) midway on front margin. Mostly small gall-making wasps. (Cynipids.)
Fig. 356. **Family 28, CYNIPIDAE**

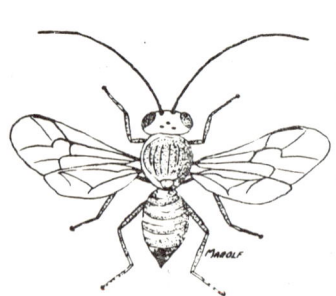

Figure 356

Fig. 356. *Diplolepis rosae* (L.)
The Mossy Rose Gall.

Head, thorax, and antennae black. Wings brownish. May be readily reared in large numbers by enclosing mossy rose galls in a tight container. Length about 4 mm.

These little fellows have some peculiar ways of making a living. There has been much speculation as to just what causes the plant so greatly to increase its grown of tissue in producing a gall and whether the magic cause could not be applied to fruits and stems to grow apples as big as nail kegs or potatoes the size of watermelons.

14b Front wings with a dark thickened spot (stigma) midway on front margin; females often with long thread-like ovipositors. 15

15a The more or less compressed abdomen attached by slender base to top of thorax instead of end, and held aloft somewhat, flag-like. (Ensign Wasps) Fig. 357.   **Family 41, EVANIIDAE**

Figure 357

Fig. 357. *Evània appendigáster* L.

Black 10-12 mm. Parasitic in the eggs of cockroaches.

The family contains some 200 species many of them in the Southern Hemisphere. The way the abdomen is attached and carried has given these wasps their name.

15b Abdomen attached to end of thorax in normal way. 16

16a Cells M1 and 1st M2 (Fig. 358) of front wings distinct. (Ichneumon Wasps.) Fig. 359. **Family 13, ICHNEUMONIDAE**

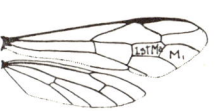

Figure 358

Fig. 359. *Megarhýssa lunàtor* Fab.

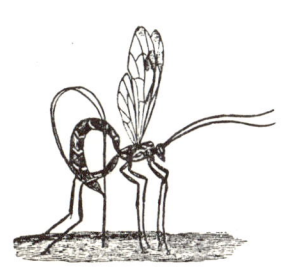

Figure 359

Light chestnut brown. Abdomen with row of V-shaped yellow marks on each side, these bordered with black. Darkened areas on wings brown. A parasite of the Pigeon-Tremex. Length of body 22-40 mm.

This large family includes some small wasps, but most of its members are of medium or large size. They are mostly parasitic on caterpillars or other insect larvae and thus do a valuable piece of work in keeping these pests from becoming too numerous.

We likely could not compete at all with the injurious insects if it were not for the many predacious and parasitic species which fight on our side. This family of 10,000 or more known species is one of the highly helpful ones. Foreign species have been frequently introduced to aid in controlling some serious pest. The European Corn Borer is a good example. Such methods of "biological control" offer our most hopeful means of handling many insect pests.

16b Cells M1 and 1st M2 fused into one cell. (Fig. 360) (Braconid Wasps.) Fig. 361.
  Family 12, BRACÓNIDAE

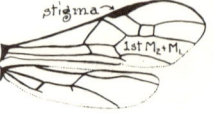

Figure 360

Fig. 361. *Chelònus texànus* Cress.

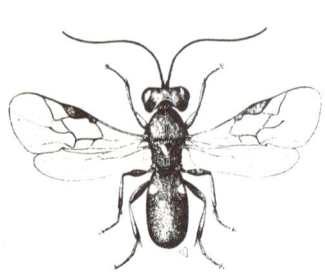

Figure 361

Head, thorax, abdomen and antennae dull black; two sub-basal spots on abdomen, yellowish white. Wings whitish. Length about 5 mm. (From U.S.D.A.)

In habits and appearance the Braconids are much like the Ichneumon wasps. Some are of medium size but most of them are small. Some are so small that they undergo their entire development within the body of a plant louse. We have counted over 500 Braconid larvae within the body of what appeared to be a fairly healthy tomato worm. The two families are distinguished by the wing characters mentioned and pictured in the key.

17a No closed cell in back wings. 18

17b Back wings with one or more closed cells. Fig. 362A. 21

Figure 362

18a Wasp-like insects with slim abdomen four or five times as long as thorax in female, (somewhat shorter in male). Antennae long (at least 14 segments) and filiform. Fig. 363.
  Family 27, PELECÍNIDAE

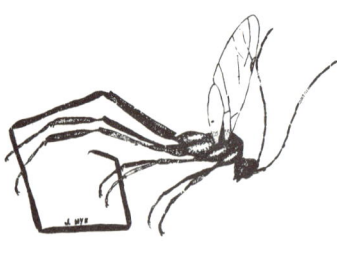

Figure 363

Fig. 363. *Pelecìnus polyturàtor* Drury

Shiny black, length about 75 mm. The female here shown is fairly common. The male, which has a much shorter abdomen, is rare. It is parasitic on white grubs.

This is a small family of what would seem to be rather primitive insects.

18b Antennae with never more than 13 segments; for the most part small insects. 19

19a Hind wing almost always with lobe at base; antennae with 13 segments; abdomen with but 2 to 4 segments (rarely 5), concave below. Metallic green, blue or purplish bee-like insects, heavily punctured. (Cuckoo-Wasps.) Fig. 364.

Family 45, CHRYSÍDIDAE

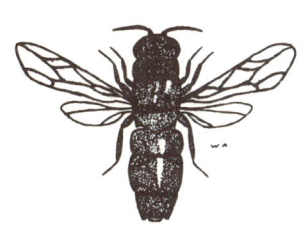

Figure 364

Fig. 364. *Chrỳsis tridens* (Lep.)

Brilliant metallic green with brassy or bluish lustre. Eyes, antennae, veins of wings and tarsi black. Length 8-11 mm.

For beauty oi coloring and sculpturing these interesting wasps are hard to beat. Most of them are a brilliant metallic green, often with blue or violet shades. The whole body is covered with large uniform punctures, which greatly enhance its beauty and interest. Like the European cuckoo, these wasps depend upon their neighbors to raise their children. The eggs are laid in the nests of wasps or bees.

19b Hind wings without lobe; antennae with never more than 12 segments; small insects, 5 mm. to less than 1 mm. **20**

20a Labial palpi with 2 to several segments; antennae of 12 or less frequently only 11 segments (if the club is one piece, then only 7 or 8 segments). Fig. 365.   Family 25, SCELIÓNIDAE

Figure 365

Fig. 365. *Eumicrósoma benéfica* Gahan Chinchbug Egg Parasite 1mm (U.S.-D.A.)

This is another family of high economic importance and contains many species of widely scattered insects. Since almost every insect may be expected to have one or more parasites the number of parasitic insects runs very large indeed. Many of them are so tiny they are not likely to be seen in the beginner's collection.

20b Labial palpi with but one segment; antennae never over 10 segments (occasionally only 8 or 9). Fig. 366.

Family 26, PLATYGÁSTERIDAE

Fig. 366. *Polygnòtus hiemàlis* Forbes Hessian Fly Parasite. (U.S.D.A.)

Here is another large family of widely distributed little parasites. Black and brown are the prevailing colors, often with bright colored markings. This tiny world is a gayly dressed one.

Figure 366

21a First segment of hind tarsus longer and wider, more or less flattened, and usually covered with hairs for carrying pollen. (Bees.) **26**

21b First segment of hind tarsus usually nearly naked and cylindric. (Wasps.) **22**

22a Pronotum touching the tegulae (Fig. 367A). **23**

Figure 367

22b Pronotum not touching the tegulae (Fig. 367B) (Typical Sphecoid Wasps.) Fig. 368.

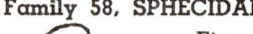

Family 58, SPHECIDAE

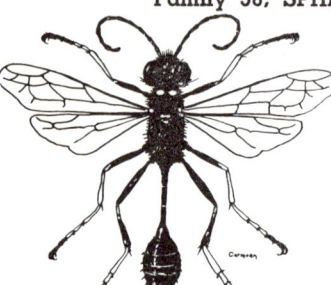

Figure 368

Fig. 368. *Sceliphron coementàrium* (Dru.)

The Black and Yellow Mud-Dauber.

Black, marked on thorax, legs and abdomen with bands of yellow. Wings yellowish brown. Builds nests of clay which it provisions with spiders. Length 20-28 mm.

Nest building takes many forms with the Sphecoids. Some burrow, some dig in the stems of plants, some are masons, while others look for a suitable hole to provision. Caterpillars and spiders are the usual food. Some tend their nests and feed the larvae as they grow; the more usual scheme is to fill the nest with food and let the young help themselves.

23a Wings not folded longitudinally when at rest. **24**

23b Wings folded once longitudinally when at rest. Eyes with notch on inner side. (Typical Wasps.) Fig. 369.   Family 55, VESPIDAE

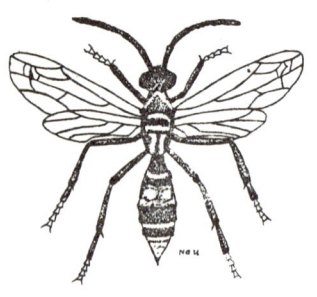

Figure 369

Fig. 369. *Polistes variàtus* Cresson

Head and thorax black, marked with brown. Abdomen blackish with yellow margins on the antennal segments and often reddish yellow spots on sides. A very common wasp or hornet which builds a flat paper nest and invades houses at the approach of cold weather. Length 17-22 mm.

Some of the Vespids are social wasps and build large nests which house a fairly sizable colony by the latter part of the summer. In our region only the fertile young queens go through the winter, so that nest building and colony raising starts all over every spring. Many species of the family are solitary, and after building and provisioning a nest and placing a few eggs in it give it no further attention.

**24a Coxae very large and long; legs much lengthened, the hind fe-
mora when extended reaching almost to the tip of the abdomen;
wings usually dark. Eyes not notched. (Spider Wasps.)
Fig. 370.**   **Family 42, PSAMMOCHARIDAE**

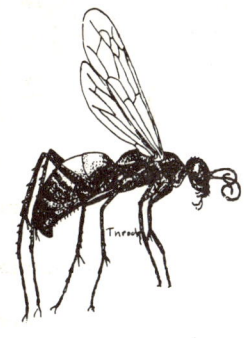

Figure 370

Fig. 370. *Psammochàrus americànus*
Pal. de Beauv.

Dull black, dorsal part of first and second
abdominal segments brick red. Wings smoky.
Length 12-14 mm.

These wasps use spiders that have been
paralyzed by stinging, in provisioning their
nests. The nests are usually in burrows in
the ground but some are made of clay. The
family is a fairly large one and some very
large wasps belong to it.

Figure 371

**24b Legs shorter, the tips of the hind femora
not reaching the middle of the abdomen..25**

25a Tarsal claws simple. (Fig. 371). (Scoliids) Fig. 372.
             Family 51, SCOLIIDAE

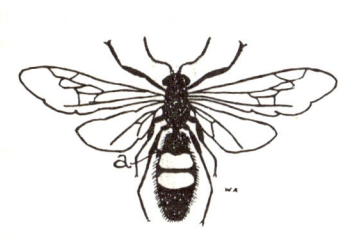

Figure 372

Fig. 372. *Scòlia bicincta* Fab.

Black, shining with bluish or
purplish sheen. Abdomen with
two broad golden yellow bands.
Wings dark. Length 21-25 mm

These wasps and some mem-
bers of the next family locate
white grubs, the larvae of May
beetles, and having paralyzed the
grub by stinging, attach an egg
to it, then build a cell about the
grub and leave it where found.
The wasp larva makes its entire
development on this grub and
eventually emerges a fully mature
wasp to hunt out and destroy
more grubs.

25b Tarsal claws cleft. (Fig. 373)

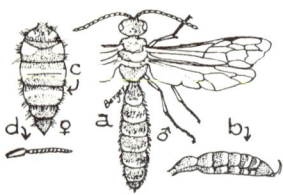

Figure 373

Fig. 374. Family 49, TIPHIIDAE

Fig. 374. *Elis quinquecincta* (Fab.)

(a, adult male; b, abdomen of male, side view; c, abdomen of female; d, antenna of female.)

Glossy black with markings on head, thorax and abdomen, bright yellow. (Yellow changes to red if left too long in a cyanide bottle.) Antennae and legs of female, yellowish brown. Antennae of male dull grayish black; legs black at base, yellowish brown at apex. Male with upturned black spine at tip of abdomen. Both sexes partly covered with gray hairs; wings dark. Length 16-23 mm.

Figure 374

Often very abundant on sweet clover in late summer.

26a Cheeks broad; eyes remote from base of mandibles. First segment of hind tarsus flattened. 27

26b Cheeks narrow; base of mandibles close to eyes. First segment of hind tarsus not much flattened. 28

27a Hind tibiae with apical spurs; eyes bare. (Bumble Bees). Fig. 375. Family 62, BOMBIDAE

Figure 375

Fig. 375. *Bombus separatus* Cress.

Black marked with yellow as pictured. 15-25 mm.

Almost every one recognizes a bumblebee at sight. They are practically harmless except when their nest is disturbed then they fight viciously to protect their home as any good citizen should. They do a valuable work in pollinating our plants. There are perhaps less than a hundred species in our country.

Country children find some exciting fun in "fighting out" a nest of bumble bees. They sometimes talk enthusiastically about "getting the honey." In fact bumble bees store very little honey but collect it as it is needed. Only the young fertile queens live through the winter and they do not feed then. In the spring they start a new nest and raise nothing but female workers until fall when males and young queens appear.

27b Hind tibiae without apical spurs; eyes hairy. (Honey Bees.)
  Fig. 376.   **Family 63, APIDAE**

Figure 376

Fig. 376. *Apis mellifera* L.

The Honey Bee. (a, Worker; b, queen; c, drone.)

There are several strains, which vary in color and size, bred by bee keepers. Length of worker 12-15 mm. Males (drones) have large eyes and are larger than workers. The queens look much like the workers but are considerably longer. (From U.S.D.A.)

The world knows only 3 or 4 species of this family. But this one species is known in the United States. It plays a highly important part in our economic life. Besides their honey and wax, this insect is the most dependable pollinator of many of our plants. A pound of honey has cost its makers, flight equivalent to twice around the world for one bee.

28a Front wing with three submarginal cells (a) (a few have only two). Tongue always pointed and either long or short. (Andrenids) Fig. 377.   **Family 60, ANDRENIDAE**

Fig. 377. *Halictus virescens* (Fab.)

Figure 377

Head and thorax brilliant metallic green; sides covered with whitish hairs; antennae and eyes black. Abdomen black; basal part of each segment ringed with whitish hairs. Legs covered with light brown hairs; often loaded with pollen. Length 11-13 mm.

A great number of our bees belong here. Some are medium size or larger; many are comparatively small. Their nesting sites are varied. Pollen is used for stored food and in collecting it, the plants profit in pollination.

28b Front wings with but two submarginal cells (a). Pollen brush on ventral side of abdomen of female. (Leaf-cutter Bees.) Fig. 378. Family 61, MEGACHILIDAE

Figure 378

Fig. 378. *Osmia lignaria* Say

Dark bluish green, shining. Covered in parts with long whitish hairs. Legs, eyes, and antennae black. Length 8-12 mm.

Everyone has noticed the round holes cut in leaves of roses and other plants. The petals of flowers show the same mutilations. These circular pieces are used to line the nests. It is well worth waiting quite a while to see how deftly and quickly the bee cuts out her leaf circle, then catches it up and is gone with it. Not all the members of the family build their nests in this way.

THE ORDERS AND FAMILIES OF INSECTS

SYSTEMATIC entomologists do not wholly agree on the arrangement of orders and families. As further study is given to the groups, changes are often found desirable. The following list is an attempt to present a conservative arrangement similar to the ones in most general use. Since we and many others have used the list as it appeared in the first edition for numbering our collections and records, we have kept the changes of these numbers to a minimum.

The figures following each order-heading shows the approximate number of known species of that order for the whole world. It is followed by a similar estimate for the United States. The numbers were for the most part furnished by C. F. W. Muesebeck and are conservative but rather close estimates. It should be born in mind that these figures represent only the named species and that the numbers are being enlarged all the while by the discovery and naming of species new to science. About 10,000 new species are thus being added each year. The numbers of undiscovered species of insects in many groups is doubtless much greater than the species now known, bewildering large as this is.

Brief hints about mounting specimens are given for each order, and places to look for the insects are often mentioned.

0. Order PROTÙRA (The Proturans) 70-28

These very small, slender, wingless insects have in comparatively recent years been discovered and given order significance. (We have numbered the order "0" to avoid confusion, since this order does not appear in our earlier editions.)

They are found in moist soil, in decaying leaves, under stones in damp places and under the bark of trees. They should be collected in 70 to 80% alcohol and mounted on microscope slides in balsam or other mounting media.

1. Eosentómidae...... With small trachea and 2 pairs of spiracles, and a pair of two-segmented vestigial appendages on ventral surface of basal abdominal segments.

2. Acerentómidae..... No trachea or spiracles; tranverse sutures on dorsal segments of abdomen.

3. Protentómidae......Without transverse sutures on upper abdominal segments; no trachea or spiracles.

I. Order THYSANÙRA (The Bristletails) 400-42

The larger species are sometimes pinned or mounted on points but are really too fragile to be treated in this way. The smaller species should always be mounted on slides, and all of the members of the order are better when thus mounted. Riker or plastic mounts are excellent for the larger specimens if very carefully done.

1. Machílidae.........Active leaping forms about one-half inch long. Found in soil and damp places.
2. Lepísmidae........ Silverfish, Firebrats. Soft, thickly-scaled; about one-half inch long. In old papers, starched clothing, leaves, etc.
3. Campodèidae...... Small, white; under stones and other damp places.
4. Projapýgidae...... Small; blind; mostly tropical.
5. Iapýgidae.........Delicate, 1/6 to 2 inches; with posterior forceps; under stones.

II. Order COLLÉMBOLA (The Springtails) 1500-289

Collect with a small camel's-hair brush, Berlese funnel-trap or aspirator and put in 70 to 80% alcohol. Mount on microscope slides in balsam or other mounting media.

1. Podùridae.........Elongate, flat; in decaying vegetation, etc. Often on snow and water.
2. Entomobrỳidae..... Elongate, distinctly segmented; many species; sometimes on the surface of water.
3. Neélidae...........Body subglobose. Under dead bark and decaying plants.
4. Smynthùridae...... Body subglobose. Very abundant on water and in moist places.

III. Order PLECÓPTERA (The Stoneflies) 1,500-288

Stoneflies shrink and lose their shape so much in drying and are too fragile to be successfully mounted on pins. If wanted for careful study they should be collected and kept in 70 to 80% alcohol. Some would add a little glycerin to keep the specimens more pliable. A few specimens may be pinned for the beginner's collection. They can be found around water courses and come to lights on warm nights.

1. Pteronárcidae...... Large; many veins in wings.
2. Pérlidae.......... Fewer veins in wings; around water; our largest family.
3. Nemoùridae........Usually small dusky species.
4. Capnìidae.........Small, dark; often on snow in early spring.

IV. Order EPHEMEROPTERA (The Mayflies) 1,500-544

What is said above for collecting and mounting Stoneflies applies equally well for Mayflies. They may be collected from shrubbery, etc., in the neighborhood of water-courses. On an occasional warm night they fly in immense numbers to street lights and show windows. The living specimens, if but recently emerged should be caged for several hours until they make their second molt, as the adults and not the winged subimagos are desired for accurate identification.

1. Polymitárcidae..... With three caudal filaments.
2. Epheméridae....... With three filaments; male claspers with four segments.
3. Potamánthidae..... Front legs of males very long.
4. Oligoneuriéllidae... Wings with few veins.
5. Baétidae.......... Wings with few cross veins.
6. Caénidae.......... No hind wings; three filaments. Often very small.
7. Leptophlebìidae.... Wings with many fine veins; hind wings small.
8. Ephemeréllidae.....Male claspers with three segments; hind wings very small.
9. Ecdyúridae........ Wings many veined.
10. Siphlonúridae..... Hind wings small; two fillaments.
11. Baetíscidae....... Rather rare.

V. Order ODONATA (The Dragonflies and Damselflies) 5,000-406

It is difficult to retain the living colors in many Odonata. If a long slender needle threaded with darning or crochet floss that matches the color of the specimen is carefully passed through the thorax and abdomen from front to back, it will be noted that the first few inches of thread draws out the abdominal contents. If this thread is then cut at each end and allowed to remain in place it will greatly strengthen the specimen as well as aid in retaining the color. The wings of both dragonflies and damselflies should be carefully spread on a pinning board and permitted to dry. A net and considerable patience and skill are necessary to catch them. They "roost" at night in tall grass and weeds near water, and may be gathered by use of a flashlight and fingers.

1. Aéschnidae........ The Aeschnids. Some of our largest dragonflies.
2. Libellùlidae........ The Skimmers. Many of our most common dragonflies belong here.
3. Agriónidae.........The True Agrionids. Broad winged, metallic colors.
4. Coenagriónidae.... The Stalked-winged Damselflies. Delicate winged; about water.

VI. Order EMBIÓPTERA (The Webspinners) 150-7

Mostly tropical or sub-tropical; living in colonies within webs on or in the ground.

1. Anisembiidae...... A few North American species.
2. Oligembiidae...... A few native species.
3. Oligotómidae...... Introduced into our Southern States.

VII. Order ORTHÓPTERA 22,000-1,172

It is customary in mounting winged Orthoptera to spread the left wings and to leave those on the right side in their normal resting position. Very fleshy specimens may have the abdomen split on its midventral part and the contents replaced with a tiny roll of cotton.

1. Bláttidae. .... The Cockroaches. Much flattened, non-leaping, omnivorous.
2. Mántidae......... The Praying Mantes. Predacious on other insects.
3. Phásmidae........ The Walkingsticks. Long and slim; wingless in our areas; herbivorous.
4. Locústidae... ..... The Short-horned grasshoppers. Antennae shorter than body; herbivorous.
5. Tettigídae......... The Grouse Locusts. Small, with long, tapering pronotum. Hibernate in adult stage.
6. Tettigoniidae. ..... The Long-horned Grasshoppers. Frequently green; long thread-like antennae; herbivorous.
7. Grýllidae......... The Crickets. Omnivorous.

VIII. Order ZORÁPTERA (The Zorapterans) 20-2

These tiny colonial insects are found in the tropics and sub-tropics.
1. Zorotýpidae.   . Our species in Florida and in Texas.

IX. Order ISÓPTERA (The Termites) 1,900-59

Termites are mostly tropical; a few species are distributed through much of our range. Their soft bodies require that they be collected in a liquid preservative and mounted on microscope slides. For the beginner's collection a few specimens may be mounted on points to represent the order. Carpenters can often tell you whose house has them. They are sometimes found in decaying logs in the timber.

1. Mastotermítidae.. . Sexes similar; Australia.
2. Hodotermítidae..... Large termites; Africa and Asia.
3. Kalotermítidae..... No workers, nymphs doing the work; feed on wood; in our southern areas.
4. Rhinotermítidae.... Subterranean and damp wood feeders; very destructive; throughout our region.
5. Termítidae.. ...... Subterranean root feeders; mostly tropical.

ORDERS AND FAMILIES

X. Order DERMÁPTERA (The Earwigs) 1,000-15

These insects are hard-shelled like the beetles and are mounted in the same way. They are nocturnal and are taken flying at lights or under stones, boards, in garbage, etc.

1. Apachyidae........Tropical; often bright colored.
2. Pygidicranidae.....Large oriental species.
3. Labidúridae........Several species cosmopolitan.
4. Labiidae..........Mostly flattened; some widely distributed.
5. Chelisóchidae......With heavy body; tropics of Eastern Hemisphere but introduced into our area.
6. Forficùlidae........Widely distributed; a large family.

XI. Order COLEÓPTERA (The Beetles) 264,000-26,276

Medium and large specimens are pinned through the right wing cover. Very large fleshy specimens are sometimes separated between thorax and abdomen and the soft contents removed after which the two parts are glued together. Small beetles are mounted on points with the bent tip of the point glued to the right side of the insect. (See Fig. 31) Beetles may be collected in alcohol and kept there indefinitely before mounting.

1. Cicindélidae..... The Tiger Beetles. Very active, usually brilliantly colored; eat insects.
2. Carábidae....... Ground Beetles. Eat insects.
3. Amphizòidae..... Fresh water aquatic beetles. Western.
4. Omophrónidae... The Round Sand Beetles. In holes on banks of streams and ponds.
5. Halíplidae....... The Crawling Water Beetles. Small; in ponds and streams. Carnivorous.
6. Dytíscidae....... The Predacious Diving Beetles. Carnivorous.
7. Gyrínidae........The Whirligig Beetles. On surface of water. Predacious.
8. Hydrophílidae.... The Water Scavenger Beetles. Mostly in water; some predacious, mostly scavengers.
9. Platypsýllidae.... The Beaver Parasite. Found on beavers; but one species.
10. Brathínidae...... Rare; small; in moss.
11. Leptinidae....... The Mammal-nest Beetles. Very small; in nests of mice and bumble bees.
12. Sílphidae........ The Carrion Beetles. Medium to large; eat decaying flesh, etc.
13. Clámbidae....... Very small; in decaying vegetation.

14. Scydmáenidae... Very small; under bark or stones or in ants' nests.

15. Orthopéridae..... Very small; in decaying vegetation.

16. Staphylínidae.... The Rove Beetles. Slender, elytra very short; scavengers.

17. Pseláphidae...... Very small; similar to rove beetles but with fewer abdominal segments.

18. Clavigéridae..... The Ant-loving Beetles. Similar to rove beetles, but only 2 joints to the antennae.

19. Ptiliidae......... The Feather-winged Beetles. Includes the smallest beetles known. In ant nests, in dead wood and leaves, etc.

20. Sphaeriidae...... Very tiny; on mud or under stones.

21. Scaphidiidae..... The Shining Fungus-Beetles. In fungi, dead wood, etc. Tip of abdomen conical.

22. Sphaerítidae..... Resemble Hister Beetles. Western.

23. Histéridae........The Hister Beetles. Hard, round, shiny, mostly black. In carrion, dung, garbage, etc.

24. Lýcidae..........The Net-winged Beetles. Flat, broad, flexible wings; diurnal; carnivorous.

25. Lampýridae..... The Firefly Beetles. Soft bodies; nocturnal, carnivorous.

26. Phengódidae..... Similar to fireflies. Females often larviform.

27. Cantháridae..... The Soldier Beetles. Long, slim, thin-winged; on flowers; carnivorous.

28. Melýridae....... The Soft-winged Flower Beetles. Taken by sweeping.

29. Cléridae......... The Checkered Beetles. Usually brilliant pattern; on tree trunks and flowers; predacious.

30. Corynétidae...... Similar to checkered beetles; feed on animal and cereal products.

31. Lymexýlidae..... Rare; elongate; narrow; wood borers.

32. Telegeùsidae... Western.

33. Micromálthidae...Rare; in decaying logs.

34. Cupésidae....... Rare; under bark.

35. Cephalòidae..... Small family; mostly western.

36. Oedeméridae.....On plants or in ground or in wood.

37. Mordéllidae......The Tumbling Flower Beetles. Wedge shaped; common on flowers.

38. Rhipiphóridae.... Wedge shaped; on flowers.

39. Melòidae........The Blister Beetles. Long, slim, with narrow necks.

40. Eurystéthidae.....Small family. Western.

41. Othnìidae.......Small family of small predacious beetles.

42. Pýthidae........The Pythenid Bark Beetles. Under bark and stones.

43. Pyrochròidae.....The Fire-colored Beetles. Usually black and red; with distinct neck. On flowers.

44. Pedílidae........ Tree-living Beetles.

45. Anthícidae.......The Ant-like Flower Beetles. Predacious; live on ground, and in flowers.

46. Euglénidae.......Very small; on leaves and flowers.

47. Cerophýtidae.....Small family of rare beetles.

48. Cebriónidae......Southern habitat.

49. Plastocéridae.....Found in South.

50. Rhipicéridae..... The Cedar Beetles. Antennae flabellate in males.

51. Élatéridae........The Click Beetles. The adults of wire worms; slim, usually with spines on hind angles of thorax.

52. Eucnémidae......Under bark and on leaves.

53. Thróscidae.......Small family of small beetles resembling the click beetles.

54. Bupréstidae...... The Metallic Wood Borers. Look as though made of metal.

55. Psephénidae..... Small family, mostly western; on wood.

56. Dryópidae....... Small water beetles.

57. Hélmidae........ In damp places.

58. Heterocéridae.... The Variegated Mudloving Beetles. In damp places.

59. Georýssidae......The Minute Mudloving Beetles. On banks of streams.

60. Dascíllidae.......The Soft-bodied Plant Beetles. On plants near water.

61. Eucinétidae...... Small family.

62. Helódidae. ......On plants near water. Small beetles.

63. Chelonarìdae.....Southern.

64. Derméstidae..... The Skin Beetles. Round or cylindrical and covered with scales. Pests of clothing, insect collections, etc.

65. Býrrhidae.. ...The Pill Beetles. At roots of trees and grass.

66. Nosodéndridae... Small family, under bark.

67. Rhysódidae...... Small. Found under bark.

68. Ostomátidae..... The Bark-gnawing Beetles. Mostly black, flattened beetles.

69. Nitidùlidae....... The Sap-feeding Beetles. Oval, somewhat flattened; under bark, in garbage, etc.

70. Rhizophágidae... Under bark, small.

71. Monotómidae.... Small; under bark and in nests of ants.

72. Cucùjidae........The Cucujids. Mostly elongate and very flat. Under bark and in grain.

73. Erotýlidae........The Erotylids. Shiny; black and red or blue and red. Often in fungi.

74. Derodóntidae.....Small family of small brown beetles.

75. Cryptophágidae.. Very small, yellowish brown; in fungi.

76. Bytùridae........ Small family; on flowers and fruits.

77. Mycetophágidae..The Hairy Fungus Beetles. Elongate; in fungi and under bark.

78. Colydìidae....... Small, dark; in fungi and dead wood.

79. Murmidìidae..... Small, oval.

80. Monoédidae......Florida.

81. Lathridìidae...... Very small; under bark and stones.

82. Mycetaèidae..... Small family; fungus feeders.

83. Endomýchidae... The Handsome Fungus Beetles. In fungi or under bark.

84. Phalácridae...... Shining Flower Beetles. Very small; convex; on flowers and under bark.

85. Coccinéllidae.....The Lady Beetles. Feed on aphids and scale insects; a few plant feeders.

86. Allecùlidae.......The Comb-clawed Bark Beetles. Elongate, brown, without spots.

87. Tenebriónidae....The Darkling Beetles. Mostly medium to large; black or gray. Largely western.

88. Lagriìdae........ The Lagriid Bark Beetles. Elongate, often metallic.

89. Monómmidae.... In bark.

90. Melandrỳidae.... The Melandryid Bark Beetles. Under bark and in fungi.

91. Ptínidae......... The Drug Store Beetles. Small pests of stored provisions.

92. Anobìidae....... The Death Watch Beetles. Very small, mostly cylindrical; in wood.

93. Bostrichidae......The Powder Post Beetles. Cylindrical, dark; in dry wood.

94. Lyctidae.........Dark, head prominent; bore in wood.

95. Sphindidae......Small species in dry fungi on trees and logs.

96. Cisidae..........Very small, in bark of trees.

97. Scarabaeidae....The Lamellicon Beetles. Dung Beetles, May Beetles, etc. Large family. The largest known beetles belong here.

98. Trogidae.........The Skin Beetles. Dark colored, roughened; feed on dried animal matter.

99. Lucanidae.......The Stag Beetles. Large, pinching jaws.

100. Passalidae.......Shiny black, large, flattened; in decaying wood.

101. Cerambycidae... The Long-horned Beetles. Cylindrical long antennae, often brightly colored; larvae bore in wood.

102. Chrysomelidae... The Leaf Beetles. Usually thickened oval forms feeding both as adults and larvae on plants.

103. Brucidae........ The Bean Weevils; in seeds of leguminous plants.

104. Brentidae........ The Primitive Weevils. Long cylindrical, males with heavy, blunt jaws.

105. Belidae.......... The New York Weevil. But one species; damages fruit trees.

106. Platystomidae....The Fungus Weevils. In bracket fungi.

107. Curculionidae....The Typical Snout Beetles. Mouthparts elongated into a snout. Larvae weevils in seeds and fruit. A very large family.

108. Platypodidae.....Small family; make pinholes in lumber.

109. Scolytidae....... The Engraver Beetles. Small, mostly in cambium of trees.

XII. Order STREPSIPTERA (The Twisted-winged Insects) 250-50

Since the females of most species never leave their host, the "stylopized" host may be pinned in the usual way, or the females removed, cleared, and mounted on microscope slides. The males can be reared to their somewhat beetle-like adult stage and mounted on points the same as with small beetles.

1. Mengeidae.........Adult females, larvae-like and free living.

2. Myrmecolacidae....Host, ants; small family.

3. Stylopidae.........Parasitic on bees and wasps; an important family.

4. Halictophágidae....Host, crickets, true bugs and Homoptera.
5. Callipharixénidae...Host, stink bugs and shield bugs.
6. Stichotremátidae....Host, Orthoptera.

XIII. Order THYSANÓPTERA (The Thrips) 3,100-594

These tiny creatures are altogether too abundant among the floral parts of many species of flowers. They may be shaken out on a white cloth (one's shirt sleeve is a handy place) and removed to a small vial of alcohol by use of a camel-hair brush. The species of plant should be recorded on the pencilled label put inside the bottle. They should be cleared and mounted on microscope slides.

1. Aelothrípidae...... Front wings strongly veined, female with saw-like ovipositor.
2. Thrípidae.......... Front wings poorly developed, female with saw-like ovipositor.
3. Merothrípidae...... Small family; under bark.
4. Phloeothrípidae.... Front wings weakly developed, female without saw-like ovipositor.
5. Idolothrípidae...... Large, slow-moving.

XIV. Order CORRODÉNTIA (The Psocids, Book Lice, etc.) 1,000-96

To collect, sweep trees, shrubs, etc. and look under stones, on rocks, fence posts, in caves, on and under bark, in dry moss and lichens, under sheath of dried corn stalks, at street or window lights, in stored papers and food products, etc. Preserve in 70-80% grain alcohol.

While some species are large enough to be successfully mounted on points, they are so soft that shrinkage interfers with their study. To keep them in vials of preservative or mount them on microscope slides is better.

1. Psócidae........... The Psocids. Wings much longer than body, on trees, fences, etc. Feed on lichens, dead insects, etc.
2. Caeciliidae........ Tarsi 2 jointed; discoidal cell of wing open.
3. Myopsócidae....... In damp places, on lichens, etc.
4. Mesopsócidae...... Tarsi 3-jointed.
5. Lepidopsócidae..... Small family.
6. Psyllipsócidae...... Found throughout the year.
7. Psoquíllidae........ In old papers and books.
8. Atrópidae.......... The death watch; in old papers.
9. Liposcélidae........ In old books or in wood.

ORDERS AND FAMILIES

XV. Order MALLÓPHAGA (The Biting Lice) 2,800-308

These parasites run rapidly among the feathers and hairs of their bird and mammal hosts and may be picked out if one has sufficient skill or patience. If the host is to be killed, if wrapped in paper or cloth, the lice often leave their host after its death and may be found within the wrappings. Mount on microscope slides.

1. Menopónidae...... Chicken lice and other bird lice.
2. Trimenopónidae.... On rodents and marsupials. Only five pairs of abdominal spiracles.
3. Ricinidae.......... All tarsi two-clawed. On humming and perching birds.
4. Laemobothriidae.... All tarsi two-clawed. On birds of prey and on water birds.
5. Gyrópidae......... Found on guinea pigs and other rodents.
6. Philothéridae....... The largest family of biting lice. No maxillary palpi. On birds.
7. Trichophiloptéridae. On mammals.
8. Trichodéctidae..... Antennae three-segmented. On domestic and other mammals.

XVI. Order ANOPLURA (The True Lice) 300-35

Collect from their mammalian host and mount on microscope slides.

1. Echinophthiriidae... On seals and walrusses.
2. Pediculidae........ Lice infesting man; eyes comparatively large.
3. Haematopínidae.... Eyes vestigial or wanting; on domestic and wild mammals.
4. Haematopinoididae. Hosts, gophers and monkeys.
5. Phthiridae......... Hosts, man and gorilla.

XVII. Order HEMÍPTERA (The True Bugs) 52,000-8,186*

Medium and large specimens should be pinned through the scutellum, a bit to the right of its middle. Small specimens should be pointed the same as beetles.

*Some systematists combine the Hemiptera and the Homoptera into one order. These figures are for the two orders thus counted together.

1. Scutelléridae...... The Shield-backed Bugs. Turtle-shaped, on plants.
2. Cýdnidae......... The Nego Bugs and Burrowing Bugs. Black or dark brown.
3. Pentatómidae...... The Stink Bugs. Some plant eating, others predacious.

4. Coreidae.........The Squash Bug Family. Destructive, plant-eating.

5. Aradidae........The Flat Bugs. Dark, much flattened; under bark.

6. Neididae.........The Stilt Bugs. Very slim, long slender legs; plant feeders.

7. Lygaeidae........The Chinch Bug Family. Live on plants.

8. Pyrrhocóridae.....The Cotton Stainer Family. Plant feeders.

9. Tingitidae........The Lace Bugs. Easily told by gauzy wings. On leaves of many plants.

10. Enicocephálidae.. The Unique-headed Bugs. Small family; predacious.

11. Phymatidae   ..The Ambush Bugs. Hide in flowers to catch bees and flies.

12. Reduviidae.   ...The Assassin Bugs. Predacious on insects and higher animals.

13. Hébridae.   ...Small plump bodies. Around stagnant water.

14. Mesoveliidae   .. Very small family of small insects.

15. Nábidae   ... The Damsel Bugs. Predacious; found on plants; slim bodies.

16. Cimicidae   ....The Bed Bugs. Parasitic on man and birds.

17. Anthocóridae.. ...The Flower Bugs. Small, on trees, flowers, etc.

18. Temitaphýdidae .. Small and rare.

19. Míridae.   ....The Plant Bugs. Suck juices of plants. A very large family.

20. Isometópidae.   ...Very small and rare.

21. Dipsocóridae...... The Jumping Ground Bugs.

22. Schizoptéridae ....Small; in damp places. This and the preceding family are often considered as one,—Cryptostemmatidae.

23. Hydrométridae.   The Water Measurers. Very slender, predacious.

24. Gérridae. ....The Water Striders. Predacious; on water.

25. Veliidae...... .. The Broad-shouldered Water Striders. On the surface of water; predacious.

26. Sáldidae.........The Shore Bugs. On damp soil; predacious.

27. Notonéctidae .. The Back Swimmers. Boat shaped, black and white. In water.

28. Naucóridae   .. The Creeping Water-bugs. Oval, flat bodied; carnivorous. In water.

29. Népidae.........The Water Scorpions. On submerged plants.
30. Belostomátidae....The Giant Water Bugs. Broad, flat, brown; carnivorous.
31. Gelastocóridae....The Toad-shaped Bugs. Body broad and short; eyes protruding. Near water.
32. Ochtéridae........The Ochterids. In mud along shore.
33. Coríxidae....   ...The Water Boatmen. Mostly plant feeders; prominent on banks of streams, in water and flying at lights.

XVIII. Order HOMÓPTERA*

Pin the medium and larger specimens through the prothorax, a bit to the right of the mid-line. Small specimens should be mounted on points or glued to the side of the pin. Spread wings of Cicadas.

*The figures for this order are included with the Hemiptera. See above.

1. Cicádidae.........The Cicadas of "Locusts." Large; broad heads.
2. Cercópidae.......The Froghoppers. Nymphs buried in froth on plants.
3. Membrácidae.. ...The Treehoppers. Queerly enlarged prothorax.
4. Cicadéllidae.......The Leafhoppers. Suck juices of plants.
5. Fulgóridae. ......The Lanternfly Family. Live on plants.
6. Chérmidae........The Jumping Plant Lice. Look like cicadas, but very small.
7. Aphídidae........ The Plant Lice. Soft bodied, frequently wingless.
8. Phylloxéridae..... Aphids covered with waxy powder.
9. Aleyródidae.......The Whiteflies. Tiny white pests of house plants.
10. Cóccidae.........The Scale Insects, Bark Lice, Mealy Bugs, etc.

XIX. Order NEURÓPTERA (The Nerve-winged Insects) 5,000-330

The very small specimens are mounted on points; others are pinned through the thorax and should have their wings spread.

1. Siálidae.......... The Alderflies, Dobsonflies, etc.
2. Raphidìidae.. ....The Snakeflies. Prothorax greatly elongate. Western.
3. Mantíspidae......The Mantis-like Neuroptera. Front legs fitted for seizing prey.
4. Sisýridae. ....The Spongilla Flies. Broad, smoky brown wings; around water.
5. Sympherobìidae...Small brownish lacewings; predacious on mealy bugs and other small insects.
6. Hemerobìidae.....The Brown Lacewings. Dark to yellow with hyaline or pale yellow wings.

7. Beróthidae........ The Beaded Lacewings. Small family.

8. Polystoechótidae...The Large Lacewings. A small family.

9. Chrysópidae...... The Green Lacewings. Larvae feed on aphids.

10. Myrmeleónidae....The Ant Lions. Delicate-winged, resembling damselflies.

11. Ascaláphidae..... The Ascalaphids. Resemble dragonflies but with long, clubbed antennae.

12. Coniopterýgidae...The Mealy-winged Neuroptera; small, less than 3 mm. long.

XX. Order TRICHÓPTERA (The Caddisflies) 4,200-782

Some favor pinning through the thorax and spreading the wings. Others think they should be kept in alcohol or other liquid preservative.

1. Rhyacophílidae....The Primitive Caddisflies. Larvae in rapid-flowing streams.

2. Hydroptílidae..... The Micro-caddisflies. Very small; resembling tineid moths.

3. Philopotámidae....Larvae in rapid-flowing water.

4. Hydropsýchidae...The Seine-making Caddisflies. Larvae in rapid streams.

5. Polycentrópidae...Larvae in slowly flowing water.

6. Psychomyìidae....In swift-water, ponds and lakes.

7. Calamocerátidae..Small family. Builds cylindrical cases.

8. Odontocéridae....Live in swift streams.

9. Molánnidae....... Larvae live on sandy lake bottoms.

10. Leptocéridae...... The Long-horned Caddisflies. Wings slender; no ocelli.

11. Phryganèidae..... The Macro-caddisflies. The largest species.

12. Limnephílidae..... Two or three spurs on middle tibae; a large family.

13. Sericostomátidae.. Ocelli absent; spurs on front legs.

XXI. Order LEPIDÓPTERA (The Moths and Butterflies) 110,000-10,768

Except for the very tiny specimens, which may be mounted on points, members of this order are pinned through the prothorax and have their wings spread. Unusual care must be taken so as to not rub the scales from the wings or otherwise damage the specimens.

1. Papiliónidae...... The Swallowtail Butterflies. Large size, usually with tail like piece on back wing.

2. Piéridae.......... The Cabbage Butterfly and others of our mostly white and yellow butterflies.

3. Danàidae. .... The Milkweed Butterflies. Large; the Monarch and others.

4. Satýridae......... The Meadow Brown Butterflies. Mostly brown with numerous eye spots.

5. Nymphálidae...... The Brushfooted Butter:'!es. Fore legs reduced.

6. Libytheidae....... The Long-beaks. Long, beak-like palpi.

7. Rhiodínidae....... The Metal-marks. Small; a small family.

8. Lycaénidae....... The Gossamer-winged Butterflies. Small, usually bright colors.

9. Hesperiidae....... The Skippers. Clubbed antennae with hooks at end. Caterpillars have slender necks.

10. Sphíngidae........The Sphinx Moths. Narrow wings; act like humming birds.

11. Saturniidae....... The Giant Silkworms. Includes our largest moths.

12. Ceratocámpidae... The Royal Moths. Stout bodies, hairy, live on foliage.

13. Syntómidae....... Narrow-winged, frequently dark colored.

14. Arctiidae......... The Tiger Moths. Brilliantly marked, medium-sized moths.

15. Agarístidae....... The Foresters. Bright colored, day flyers.

16. Noctùidae.........The Owlet Moths. Cutworms and army worms.

17. Pericópidae....... Bright colored moths; larvae eat foliage.

18. Dióptidae......... Small family of uncommon species.

19. Notodóntidae......The Prominents. Tree feeders; adults medium size.

20. Thyatíridae....... Foliage feeders.

21. Lymantriidae......The Tussock Moths. Females wingless, larvae on foliage.

22. Eupterótidae...... Small family of medium sized pale gray moths.

23. Lasiocámpidae.... Tent caterpillars.

24. Bombýcidae.......The Silkworms.

25. Drepánidae....... The Drepanids. Sickle-shaped point on front wings.

26. Geométridae...... The Measuring-worms. Larvae walk with looping movement.

27. Epiplémidae.......Slender bodies, large wings.

28. Lacosómidae.....Broad wings with vestigial frenulum.

29. Psýchidae.........The Bagworm Moths. Wingless females, males winged; larvae in debris-covered silken bags.

30. Limacódidae......The Slug-caterpillar Moths. Medium to small size.

31. Megalopýgidae....The Flannel-moths. Thickly covered with scales and long curly hair.

32. Dalcéridae........Body small, wings broad.

33. Epipyrópidae......Small tropical moths.

34. Zygaénidae.......The Smoky Moths. On grapes, etc.

35. Thyrídidae........The Window-winged moths. With white or yellowish translucent spots on wings.

36. Pyrálidae.........The Pyralids. Mostly small moths, slender body, prominent head.

37. Pterophóridae.....The Plume Moths. Wings slit length-wise.

38. Orneódidae.......The Many-plumed Moths. Each wing divided into six plumes.

39. Cosmopterýgidae..Small narrow-winged moths.

40. Gelechiidae.......Grain and gall-making moths.

41. Oecophóridae.....The parsnip web worm, etc.

42. Blastobásidae.....Small moths.

43. Stenómidae.......Wings broad, especially back ones.

44. Ethmiidae........Broad wings; front ones usually bright colored.

45. Aegeriidae........The Clear-winged Moths. Resemble bees.

46. Eucósmidae......The Codling Moth and others.

47. Tortrícidae.......The Leaf Rollers. Small to medium moths, front wings square cut at outer end.

48. Phaloniidae.......Small moths.

49. Carposínidae......Small moths.

50. Heliodínidae......The Sun Moths. Narrow pointed wings, edges fringed.

51. Heliozélidae.......Sharp pointed wings; long antennae.

52. Glyphipterýgidae..Similar to Tortricids.

53. Plutéllidae........Small to medium size.

54. Yponomeútidae....The Beautiful Mining Moths. Small moths; feed on trees.

55. Haploptiliidae.....The Pistol Case Bearers, etc.

56. Elachístidae.......Small family of small moths.

57. Tischeriidae.......Mostly leaf miners.

58. Gracilariidae.....Large family; mostly small leaf miners.

59. Scythrídidae......Small, narrow-winged moths.

60. Lyonetiidae.......The Morning Glory Leafminer and others.

61. Acrolóphidae......Fairly large and heavy moths.

62. Tinéidae..........A large family; includes the clothes moths.

63. Cóssidae.........The Carpenter Moths. Spindle shaped bodies, narrow wings; larvae wood borers.

64. Nepticúlidae......The smallest of moths; wing venation much reduced.

65. Incurvariidae......Mostly miners and case bearers.
66. Adélidae.........Very small moths with very long fine antennae.
67. Prodóxidae.......The Yucca Moths, and others.
68. Micropterýgidae...The Primitive Moths. Small family of small moths.
69. Hepiálidae........The Swifts. Medium to large size, narrow wings.

XXII. Order MECÓPTERA (The Scorpionflies) 350-66

They are mounted on points or pinned with the wings spread.

1. Panórpidae........Scorpion flies. In damp woods.
2. Boreìdae..........Wingless winter forms; on moss.
3. Bittácidae.........Resemble crane flies. In woods.

XXIII. Order DÍPTERA (The Flies) 80,000-15,760

Members of this exceedingly interesting order need to be handled very carefully both in catching and mounting. They should be kept separate from other insects in the killing bottle and not many put in the bottle at one time. Liquid preservatives or wetting in any way, leaves them in wretched condition. The pin should be placed slightly to the right of the mid-line of the prothorax. Small diptera are mounted on points or glued to the side of the pin.

1. Tanydéridae......The Primitive Crane Flies. Only three species known to North America.
2. Ptychoptéridae....The False Crane Flies. Larvae in wet organic earth.
3. Trichocéridae.....The Winter Crane Flies. Sometimes abundant during warm winter days; most abundant during spring and fall.
4. Tipùlidae.........The Typical Crane Flies. A large family of fragile long-legged flies. When freshly killed put in individual small envelopes until dry, then mount on double points.
5. Anisopódidae.....Near edge of woods and swamps and on trunks of trees.
6. Blepharicéridae....The Net-winged Midges. Most abundant near fast-flowing streams.
7. Simuliidae........The Black Flies. Small, vicious, biting flies near streams.
8. Thaumalèidae.....Along the edge of streams, particularly where moss is present.
9. Chironómidae.....The Midges. Mostly harmless, mosquito-shaped insects.

10. Ceratopógonidae.. The Biting Midges. Very small, slender flies; found along water courses.

11. Psychódidae...... The Moth Flies. Tiny broad hairy-winged flies.

12. Díxidae.......... The Dixa Midges. Near running water.

13. Culícidae........ The Mosquitoes. Slender scaly winged flies.

14. Cecidomyidae.... The Gall Midges. Tiny gall-making flies.

15. Sciáridae........ The Dark Winged Fungus Gnats. Around fungi in moist places.

16. Mycetophílidae....The Fungus Gnats. Moderately small, slender flies found around fungi.

17. Bibiónidae....... The March Flies. Slender, small to medium sized flies, frequent in early spring.

18. Scatópsidae...... The Minute Black Scavengers. Tiny black or brown flies breeding in decaying vegetation.

19. Rachicéridae..... Medium sized, elongate flies.

20. Stratiomyidae..... The Soldier Flies. Often brightly marked, around flowers.

21. Coenomyiidae....Medium to large flies found in moist woods.

22. Tabánidae....... The Horse Flies. Swift-flying blood suckers.

23. Pantophthálmidae. Tropical flies.

24. Rhagiónidae...... The Snipe Flies. Small to medium sized, long-legged flies found abundantly in woods and damp places.

25. Scenopínidae.....The Window Flies. Moderate or small size, dark colored.

26. Mydàidae........The Mydas Flies. Very large elongate flies; larvae live on decayed wood.

27. Asílidae......... The Assassin or Robber Flies. Large, mostly elongate, predacious flies.

28. Therévidae.......The Stilleto Flies. Moderate sized predacious flies, most abundant in dry areas.

29. Apiocéridae......Large elongate flies; mostly western.

30. Bombyliidae......The Bee Flies. Large family of hairy flies.

31. Nemestrínidae....Moderate size; quick fliers.

32. Cýrtidae..........Thorax and abdomen large, head small.

33. Empídae..........The Dance Flies. In moist places, woods, etc.

34. Dolichópidae......The Long-headed or Long-legged Flies. Small, usually metallic green or blue.

35. Lonchoptéridae....The Pointed-winged Flies. Small, slender, brownish or yellowish flies found in moist places.

36. Phóridae.........The Hump-backed Flies. Small or very small, often wingless.

37. Platypézidae......The Flat-footed Flies. The larvae of at least part of the family live in fungi.

38. Pipunculidae......The Big-headed Flies. Readily told by the large head; larvae parasitic on other insects.

39. Sýrphidae........The Flower Flies. A large family of beneficial flies.

40. Conópidae........The Thick-headed Flies. Moderate sized, elongate flies, largely parasitic on Hymenoptera.

41. Pyrgótidae........Parasitic on beetles.

42. Otítidae..........The Pictured-winged Flies. Wings usually marked with brown, black or yellowish; common in moist places.

43. Trupanèidae......The Fruit Flies. For most part small; wings usually pictured.

44. Palloptéridae......In moist shady places; usually with pictured wings.

45. Lonchàeidae......Small, dark, shining flies.

46. Ropaloméridae....Tropical.

47. Tanypézidae......Medium sized flies with long, slender legs; in moist woods.

48. Calobátidae.......The Stilt-legged Flies. Legs very long; near moist places.

49. Micropézidae......Slender flies with long legs, in marshes and moist places.

50. Nerìidae..........Slender flies with long legs; near water.

51. Piophilidae.......Small black or bluish metallic flies. The "cheese-skipper" belongs here.

52. Sépsidae..........Small, shining, black or reddish flies; scavengers.

53. Lauxanìidae......Most commonly in moist places.

54. Periscélidae.......Small, wings sometimes pictured.

55. Drosophilidae.....The Small Fruit Flies. Small; wings often pictured. Around ripe fruit and decaying vegetation.

56. Astèiidae.........Small flies.

57. Opomýzidae......Small; wings sometimes pictured; in moist places.

58. Agromýzidae......The Leaf Miners. Small, the larvae mine the leaves of many plants.

59. Phyllomýzidae.....Small, usually black; often found sunning themselves.

60. Chlorópidae.......The Frit Flies. Small, bare; larvae live in many plant stems.

61. Ephýdridae.......The Shore Flies. Small; along marshes, swamps and water courses.

62. Canacèidae.......Very small; along sea shore.

63. Diópsidae.........The Stalked-eyed Flies. But few species known to North America.

64. Borbóridae........Small, black or brown; scavengers.

65. Clusìidae.........Wings marked with black or brown; in moist places.

66. Chamaemỳidae....Small grayish flies.

67. Tetanocéridae.....The Marsh Flies.

68. Chyromỳidae.....Small flies. Sometimes with pictured wings.

69. Megamerínidae....Tropical.

70. Psílidae..........The Carrot-rust Fly and other plant feeders.

71. Coelópidae........Along sea shores.

72. Helomýzidae......Medium size; scavengers.

73. Dryomýzidae.....Moderate size; along water courses.

74. Múscidae........The House Fly and many smaller pests.

75. Gasterophílidae...The Horse Bot Flies. One genus of but three species.

76. Metopìidae.......The Flesh Flies. Flesh feeders, parasites or scavengers.

77. Cuterébridae.....The Robust Bot Flies. Parasitic on rodents.

78. Oéstridae........The Bot Flies. Medium to large size, usually covered with long fine hairs.

79. Tachínidae.......The Tachinids. Rather heavily bristled. Parasitic on other insects.

80. Braúlidae........The Honey-bee Parasite. But one species; found in bee hives.

81. Hippobóscidae....The Bird Parasite Flies. Often wingless; the Common Sheep tick, etc.

82. Nycteribìidae.....Resemble spiders; wingless, parasitic on bats.

83. Stréblidae........The Bat Flies. Mostly parasitic on bats.

XXIV. Order SIPHONÁPTERA (The Fleas) 1,100-319

First, you catch the flea! It's easier to trick them in some way, than to run them down in the open. They may be mounted either on points or on microscope slides.

1. Pulícidae.......... Our most common fleas; pests of man and his domestic animals. Eyes usually present. Only a single row of setae on an abdominal tergite.

2. Dolichopsýllidae....The largest family of fleas. Abdominal tergites with more than one row of bristles. Many species have no eyes.

3. Hystrichopsýllidae..Mostly on rodents, some quite large.

4. Macropsýllidae.....A small family restricted to Australia and South America.

5. Ichnopsýllidae..... Confined to bats.

6. Hectopsýllidae..... Thorax very much reduced. The sticktight flea of poultry, cats, and dogs.

XXV. Order HYMENÓPTERA (The Bees, Wasps, Ants, etc.)
107,000-17,408

While somewhat less delicate than the Flies, they are caught and mounted in much the same way, except that the hunter needs to keep in mind that many of them are quite capable of defending themselves. Ants and some other hard, hairless species may be killed and kept in alcohol. Some put ants on points; others insist that they should be mounted on cards.

1. Xyélidae.......... The Xyelid Sawflies.

2. Pamphiliidae...... The Web-spinning and Leaf-rolling Sawflies.

3. Céphidae........ The Stem Sawflies. Larvae bore in stems of plants.

4. Xiphydriidae...... The Xiphydriid Sawflies. Small family of medium sized bees.

5. Sirícidae.......... The Horn-tails. Larvae are wood borers.

6. Crabrónidae...... The American Sawfly and others.

7. Árgidae.......... The Argid Sawflies. Small family infesting sweet potatoes, etc.

8. Dipriónidae....... Feed on pine and spruce.

9. Tenthredínidae.... The Typical Sawflies. Currant worm, rose slug, pear slug, etc. A large family.

10. Pterygophóridae ..Feed on oaks, hickory, etc.

11. Orússidae........The Parasitic Woodwasps. Adults very active, run on tree trunks.

12. Bracónidae........The Braconids. Small to medium sized, slender wasps; parasitic.

13. Ichneumónidae.... The Ichneumon Wasps. Some very small; mostly fairly large slender wasps; parasitic.

191

14. Trigonálidae...... Parasitic in nests of social bees.
15. Aulácidae........Mostly parasitic on Coleoptera.
16. Stephánidae......Parasitic on wood-boring insects.
17. Gasteruptiónidae.. Parasitic on solitary wasps and bees.
18. Roproniidae......Rare; parasitic.
19. Heloridae........Parasitic in cocoons of lacewings.
20. Vanhorniidae.....Small, parasitic wasps.
21. Diapriidae.......Parasitic on flies.
22. Sérphidae........Parasitic on flies and beetles.
23. Callicerótidae..... Very small family.
24. Ceraphrónidae.... Very small parasitic wasps.
25. Scelionidae...... Very important family of egg parasites.
26. Platygásteridae....Parasitic on other Hymenoptera.
27. Pelecinidae....... Large, black, wasp-like species with abdomen of female very long.
28. Cynípidae........The Cynipids. Many are gall makers.
29. Callimómidae..... Parasitic on gall makers or infest seeds.
30. Perilámpidae.....Small parasitic wasps.
31. Chalcididae....... The Chalcid Flies. Tiny parasitic bees with wing veination much reduced.
32. Eurytómidae..... The Wheat Jointworm, the Wheat Straw-worm, etc.
33. Encýrtidae........Small wasps.
34. Signiphóridae..... Small family; parasite scale insects, etc.
35. Eupélmidae....... Small egg parasites.
36. Pteromálidae......Parasitic.
37. Aphelínidae......Small wasps, parasitic on aphids and scale insects.
38. Eulóphidae........Small, parasitic on plant feeding wasps.
39. Trichogrammátidae Parasitic.
40. Mymáridae....... Very small egg parasites.
41. Evaniidae........The Ensign Wasps. Abdomen short and held erect like a flag.
42. Psammocháridae.. The Spider Wasps. Slender wasps that provision their nests with spiders.
43. Embolémidae......Rare; parasites.
44. Cléptidae........ Similar to next family.
45. Chrysídidae.......The Cuckoo-Wasps. Brilliant metallic green or blue.

46. Anthobóscidae.... Very small family.

47. Sapýgidae........ Black, spotted or banded with yellow.

48. Thýnnidae........ Australian Flower Wasps.

49. Tiphìidae........ Fairly large parasitic wasps.

50. Mutíllidae........The Velvet Ants. Females wingless, densely clothed with hair.

51. Scolìidae.........The Scoliids. Large sized wasps, parasitic on white grubs.

52. Formícidae.......The Ants. Workers wingless. Very large family.

53. Bethýlidae....... Small to medium parasitic wasps.

54. Rhopalosómidae...Very small family.

55. Véspidae........ The Hornets, etc.

56. Ampulícidae...... Uncommon; prey on cockroaches.

57. Dryínidae........Small parasitic wasps.

58. Sphècidae....... The Typical Sphecid Wasps. The common mud daubers and others.

59. Hylaèidae........The Bifid-tongued Bees. Wasp-like bees.

60. Andrénidae....... The Andrenids. Short-tongued, solitary bees. A large and important family.

61. Megachílidae..... The Leaf-cutter Bees, etc. Line their nests with neatly cut pieces of leaves or flower petals.

62. Bómbidae.........The Bumblebees. Large or medium sized. Hairy, usually black and yellow.

63. Ápidae.......... The Honey bees. Only our introduced honey maker.

INDEX AND PICTURED GLOSSARY

A

Abdomen: the third and last main division of an insect's body; bears no functional legs in the adult stage. (See Figs. 43 and 44) 43, Fig. 379.

Figure 379

Acanthoscelides
  obtectus, 98
Acerentomidae, 171
Achorutes
  armatus, 65
Acrolophidae, 186
Acrydium
  arenosum, 74
Adalia
  bipunctata, 50
Adelidae, 187
Adult, 5
Aegeriidae, 128, 186
Aelothrips
  fasciatus, 102
Aeolothripidae, 102, 180
Aerial net, 14
Aeschnidae, 72, 173
Agabus
  disintegratus, 80
Agaristidae, 185
Agonoderus
  comma, 81
Agrion
  maculatum, 71
Agrionidae, 71, 173
Agromyzidae, 152, 189
Alcohol, 37
Alderflies, 121
Aleyrodidae, 120, 183
Alleculidae, 178
Althysanus
  exitiosus, 52
Ambush Bugs, 109, 112
American Cockroach, 51
Amphicerus
  bicaudatus, 88
Amphizoidae, 175
Ampulicidae, 193
Anagrapha
  falcifera, 52
Anal cell, Fig. 380

Figure 380

Anaphoidea
  conotracheli, 54
Anasa
  tristis, 114
Anax
  junius, 72
Andrenidae, 169, 193
Angoumois Grain Moth, 130
Anisembiidae, 174
Anisopodidae, 187
Annulate or Annulated: ringed or marked with colored bands.
Anobiidae, 178
Anoplura, 105, 181
Antenna,-ae: jointed appendages borne one on each side of the head, commonly called feelers. Sensory in function. (See Fig. 43)
Antenodal: the area before the nodus, Fig. 381.

Figure 381

Anthicidae, 95, 177
Anthoboscidae, 193
Anthocoridae, 111, 112, 182
Anthrenus
  scrophulariae, 89
Ant-like Flower Beetles, 95
Ant-like Stone Beetles, 86
Ant Lions, 123
Ant-loving Beetles, 84, 98
Ants, 159
Apachyidae, 175
Apex: that part of any joint segment, or wing, that is opposite the base or point of attachment.
Aphelinidae, 162, 192
Aphididae, 120, 183
Aphids, 120.
Aphiochaeta
  perdita, 145
Aphis
  gossypii, 120
  maidi-radicis, 59
Aphis Lions, 122
Aphorista
  vittata, 96
Apical: at or near the apex.
Apidae, 169, 193
Apioceridae, 188
Apis
  mellifera, 169
Appendiculate: bearing appendages.
Apple-bug, 79
Apposition: placed one on top of another like a series of plates.
Aradidae, 110, 112, 182
Aradus
  acutus, 112

Arctiidae, 137, 185
Arctocorixa
  interrupta, 116
Argidae, 191
Argyrotaenia
  velutinana, 135
Arista: a bristle on the last segment of the antennae of flies — often plumose. Fig. 382.

Figure 382

Arthromacra
  aenea glabricollis, 92
Ascalaphidae, 123, 184
Asilidae, 145, 188
Asparagus Miner, 152
Aspidiotiphagus
  citrinus, 162
Aspidiotus
  perniciosus, 63
Aspirator, 16
Asteiidae, 189
Assassin Bugs, 108, 110
Assassin Flies, 145
Atropidae, 180
Aulacidae, 192
Author: scientist who names a new species. 1

B

Back Swimmers, 116
Baetidae, 69, 173
Baetis
  sp., 69
Baetiscidae, 173
Bagworms, 134
Bait traps, 16
Balancers: pin-like structures replacing the second wings on the Diptera. Fig. 383.

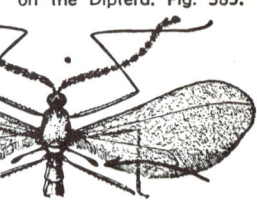

Figure 383

Balsa wood, 31
Balsam, 36
Banded Thrips, 102
Bark-gnawing Beetles, 89
Bark Lice, 119
Basal: at or pertaining to the base or point of attachment to or nearest the main body.

194

INDEX

Figure 384

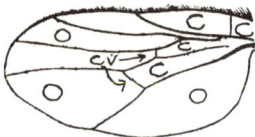
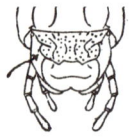

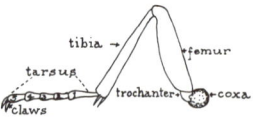
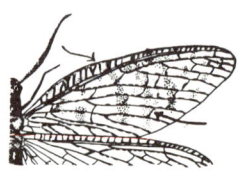
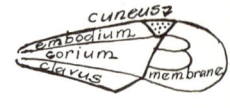

INDEX

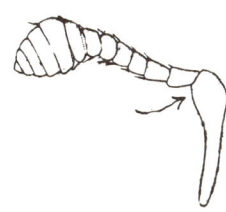

Figure 392

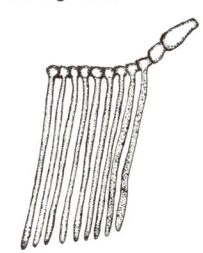

Figure 393

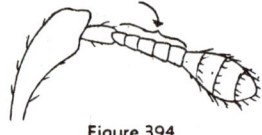

Figure 394

G

H

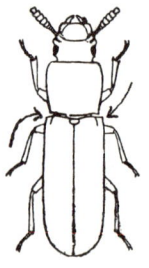

Figure 395

INDEX

I

J

K

Figure 396

L

flattened plates

Figure 397

M

199

Figure 398

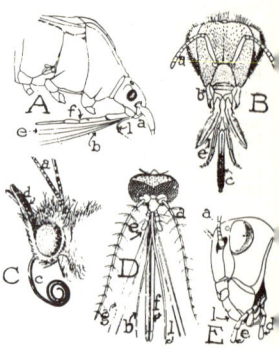

Figure 399. Mouth-parts of Insects A, Hemiptera; B, Honey bee; C, Butterfly; D, Mosquito; E, Grasshopper. a, antenna; b, mandible; c, sucking tube; d, labial palp; e, maxillary palp; f, labium; g, maxilla; i, labrum.

N

INDEX

O

Obsolete: nearly or entirely
  lost, inconspicuous.
Obtuse: not sharply pointed.
Ocellus: a simple eye, con-
  sisting of a single convex
  or bead-like lens; usually
  found on vertex; three is
  the usual number. 43 Fig.
  400.

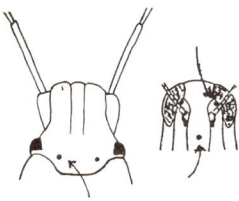

Figure 400

Omnivorous: feeding on both
  plant and animal matter.
Open Cell: wing cell extend-
  ing to margin of wing.
  (See Fig. 385)
Order, 2
Ovipositor, 45

P

Palpi: mouth feelers; sensory in function. Fig. 401.

Figure 401

Palps: often used instead of
  palpi.
Papering butterflies, 26
Paradichlorobenzine, 36
Pectinate: comb-shaped, with
  even branches like the
  teeth of a comb. (See
  Fig. 41)
Penny Bug, 79
Petiole: slender front part
  of abdomen connecting
  with thorax in wasps, etc.
  Fig. 402.

Figure 402

Phylum, 2
Piceous: pitchy black.
Pictured-wing Flies, 153

INDEX

Ranatra
  fusca, 115
Raphidiidae, 121, 183
Record card, 40
Recumbent: Lying down.
Red-banded Leaf
  Roller, 135
Red Bugs, 113
Reduviidae, 108, 110, 182
Reduvius
  personatus, 110
Reflexed: angularly bent
  backward; a surface
  turned in upon itself.
Relaxing, 27
Reticulitermes
  flavipes, 57, 58
Rhagio
  mystacea, 146
Rhagionidae, 146, 188
Rhagoletis
  cingulata, 152
Rhamphomyla
  rava, 147
Rhexidius
  canaliculatus, 98
Rhinotermitidae, 174
Rhiodinidae, 185
Rhipiceridae, 177
Rhipiphoridae, 176
Rhizophagidae, 178
Rhopalosomidae, 193
Rhyacophilidae, 184
Rhynchophora, 55
Rhysodidae, 178
Rice Weevil, 50
Ricinidae, 181
Ringlegged Earwig, 77
Rocky Mountain
  Locust, 75
Ropalomeridae, 189
Roponiidae, 192
Rose Midge, 142
Rose Slug, 159
Rove Beetles, 84
Royal Moths, 134
Rudimentary: undeveloped.
Rufous: brick red.
Rugose: wrinkled.

S

Saldidae, 111, 182
Saldula confluenta, 111
Salt-marsh Caterpillar, 137
San Jose Scale, 63
Sanded Grouse Locust, 74
Sap-feeding Beetles, 90
Sapygidae, 193
Saturniidae, 134, 185
Satyridae, 127, 185
Say Stink Bug, 107
Scale Insects, 119
Scale Parasites, 162
Scales: broad flattened hairs.
Scape: the long basal joint
  of a geniculate antenna.
  (See Fig. 41)
Scaphidiidae, 84, 176
Scaphidium
  quadriguttatum, 84
Scasabaeidae, 82, 179
Scatopsidae, 188
Scelionidae, 165, 192
Sceliphron
  coementarium, 166
Scenopinidae, 188
Schizopteridae, 182

Sciaridae, 188
Scientific names, 1
Sclerite: any piece of the
  body wall bounded by su-
  tures. 45
Scolia
  bicincta, 167
Scoliidae, 167, 193
Scolops
  sulcipes, 117
Scolytidae, 100, 179
Scolytus
  rugulosus, 100
Scorpionflies, 138
Scutelleridae, 107, 181
Scutellum: the triangular
  piece between the base
  of the elytra. Particularly
  large on some Hemiptera.
  Fig. 407.

Figure 407

Scydmaenidae, 86, 176
Scythrididae, 186
Seed Weevils, 98
Segment: a ring or division
  bounded by incisions or
  sutures.
Separator, 16
Sepsidae, 153, 189
Sericostomatidae, 184
Serphidae, 192
Serrate: saw-toothed.
Seventeen Year Cicada, 117
Sharp-nosed Leaf-
  hopper, 118
Sheep Tick, 139
Shield-backed Bugs, 107
Shining Flower Beetles, 97
Shining Fungus
  Beetles, 84
Shore Bugs, 111
Shore Flies, 150
Short-winged Scavenger
  Beetles, 84
Shot-hole Borer, 100
Sialidae, 121, 183
Sialis
  infumata, 121
Signiphoridae, 192
Silpha
  americana, 86
Silphidae, 86, 175
Silver Spotted Skipper, 125
Silverfish, 61, 64
Silver-striped Webworm, 132
Simuliidae, 142, 187
Siphlonuridae, 68, 173
Siphonaptera, 156, 190
Siricidae, 158, 191
Sisyridae, 183
Sitodiplosis
  mosellana, 47
Sitophilus
  oryzae, 50
Sitotroga
  cerealella, 130
Skimmers, 72
Skin Beetles, 82, 89

Skippers, 125
Slickers, 64
Small Earwig, 77
Smaller Water Striders, 109
Smoky Alderfly, 121
Smoky Moths, 131
Smynthuridae, 65, 172
Smynthurus
  sp., 61
Snakeflies, 121
Snipe Flies, 146
Snout Beetle, 78
Snout Moths, 132
Snowfleas, 65
Snow Scorpionflies, 138
Snowy Tree Cricket, 73
Sod Webworms, 132
Soft-winged Flower
  Beetles, 87
Soldier Beetle, 85
Soldier Flies, 144
Sparnopolius
  fulvus, 147
Species: an aggregation of
  individuals alike in ap-
  pearance and structure,
  mating freely and pro-
  dusing young which mate
  freely and produce fertile
  offspring. 1
Sphaeridium, 83
Sphaeriidae, 176
Sphaeritidae, 176
Sphecidae, 166, 193
Sphindidae, 179
Sphingidae, 131, 185
Spiders, 20
Spider Wasps, 167
Spined Soldier Bug, 51
Spiny-legged Flies, 153
Spiracles, 45
Spittle Insects, 119
Spotted Camel
  Cricket, 62
Spreading board, 34
Spring Cankerworm, 60
Springtails, 65
Spur: a short, stiff, gener-
  ally blunt process and
  usually not articulated at
  its base.
Squamae (See Fig. 317)
Squash Borer, 128
Squash Bug, 114
Stable Fly, 155
Stag Beetles, 83
Stagomantis
  carolina, 76
Staphylinidae, 84, 176
Stem-sawflies, 158
Stenomidae, 186
Stephanidae, 192
Sternum,-a: the breast; mid-
  dle portion of the under-
  surface of thorax. (See
  Fig. 44)
Stigma: an opaque thick-
  ened spot, sometimes on
  front margin of wing.
  Fig. 408.

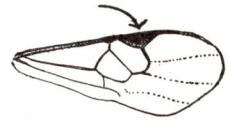

Figure 408

INDEX

Stichotrematidae, 180
Sticktight Fleas, 156
Stings, 20
Stilleto Flies, 146
Stilt Bugs, 113
Stink Bugs, 107
Stomoxys
calcitrans, 155
Stoneflies, 66
Stratiomyidae, 144, 188
Stratiomyia
meiginii, 144
Straw Worms, 161
Streblidae, 190
Strepsiptera, 51, 179
Stria,-ae: a longitudinal depressed line or furrow, frequently punctured, extending from base to apex of elytra. Fig. 409.

Figure 409

Striate,-ed: marked with parallel, fine, impressed lines.
Striped Sod Webworm, 132
Stylopid, 51, 179
Sub-: as a prefix, means that the main term is not entirely applicable, but must be understood as modified in some way.
Sub-Cylindrical: not quite cylindrical.
Sub-Depressed: partially depressed.
Sub-Erect: nearly erect.
Sub-Family: the next subordinate classification unit below family.
Sub-Humeral Spots: spots located near the humerus or shoulder.
Sugarcane Beetle, 50
Sugaring for moths, 16
Sun Flies, 153, 162
Survey, 39
Suture: a seam or impressed line indicating the division of distinct parts of the body wall; in beetles, the line of junction of elytra.
Swallow-tails, 125
Sweeping net, 12
Swordbearer, 73
Sycamore Lace Bug, 108
Sympherobiidae, 183
Syntomidae, 185
Syrphidae, 148, 189
Syrphus
ribesii, 47, 148

T

Tabanidae, 144, 188
Tabanus
lasiophthalmus, 144
Tachinidae, 154, 190
Taeniothrips
inconsequens, 54
Tanyderidae, 187
Tanypezidae, 189
Tarnished Plant Bug, 111
Tarsus-i: the foot; the jointed appendage attached at the apex of the tibia, bearing claws and pulvilli. (See Fig. 42)
Telegeusidae, 176
Telephanus
velox, 93
Tenebrio
molitor, 92
Tenebrionidae, 92, 178
Tenebroides
mauritanicus, 89
Tenthredinidae, 159, 191
Teritaphydidae, 182
Termitidae, 174
Tetanoceridae, 190
Tettigidae, 74, 174
Tettigoniidae, 73, 174
Thaumaleidae, 187
Therevidae, 146, 188
Thermobia domestica, 64
Thick-headed Flies, 154
Thorax: second region of the insect body; between head and abdomen; the dorsal covering of the prothorax is sometimes taken to mean thorax. 44
Thripidae, 102, 180
Throscidae, 177
Thyatiridae, 185
Thynnidae, 193
Thyrididae, 186
Thyridopteryx
ephemeraeformis, 134
Thysanoptera, 102, 180
Thysanura, 64, 172
Tibia: second large joint of leg; articulates with the femur. 44 (See Fig. 42)
Tiger Beetles, 80
Tiger Moths,, 137
Tiger Swallowtail, 52
Tinea
pellionella, 129
Tineidae, 129, 186
Tingitidae, 108, 182
Tiphiidae, 168, 193
Tipula
angustipennis, 140
Tipulidae, 140, 187
Tischeriidae, 186
Tmesiphorus
costalis, 84
Toad Bugs, 114
Tomentose: covered with fine hair, so matted together that the particular hairs cannot be separated.
Tooth: a short pointed process from an appendage or margin.
Tortricidae, 135, 186

Tracheal Gills: filmy respiratory organs of aquatic larvae and nymphs. Fig. 410.

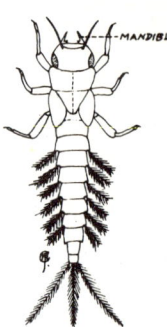

Figure 410

Traps, 15
Tray label, 39
Trays, 39
Treehoppers, 118
Tremex
columba, 158
Trialeurodes
vaporiorum, 120
Trichoceridae, 187
Trichodectes
ovis, 105
Trichodectidae, 105, 181
Trichogramma
minutum, 161
Trichogrammatidae, 161, 192
Trichophilopteridae, 181
Trichoptera, 124, 184
Trigonalidae, 192
Trimenopanidae, 181
Trimerotropis
maritima, 51
Triphleps
insidiosus, 111
Trochanter, 44
Trogidae, 82, 179
Tropaea
luna, 134
Trox
monachus, 82
True Flies, 47
True Scorpionflies, 139
Trupaneidae, 152, 189
Tumbling Flower Beetles, 95
Tussock Moths, 138
Two-spotted Ladybird, 50
Typical Sawflies, 159
Typical Snout Beetles, 101
Typical Wasps, 166
Typocerus
velutina, 97

U

Ulolodes macleayana
hageni, 123
Underwings, 137

INDEX

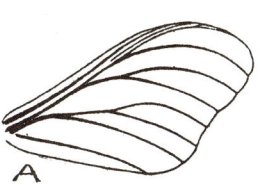

Figure 411

Worker: commonly designated by the symbol ☿ .

47140012